Name:

GCSE

or before

Essential Exam Practice

With Answers

Key Stage 4
GCSE Higher

Ruso Bradley, June Hall and Mark Haslam

020   578

Brookworth
BOOKS

Introduction

Mathematics is a subject where practice is the key to exam success. There is no better way of boosting your grade than practising the type of questions that will come up in your exams. It is no secret that many questions come up year after year, which is why the *Essential Exam Practice* range concentrates on these extremely important questions. It is also true that you can't predict exactly what will be in your exams, but if you try all the questions in this book, you are unlikely to get any nasty surprises!

About this book

This book is aimed at candidates taking the Higher tier in GCSE Mathematics, and is suitable for all examination boards.

The questions are split into four main sections:
● Number (N)
● Algebra (A)
● Shape, Space & Measures (S)
● Handling Data (H)

Within these sections, the questions are grouped by topic, so you can quickly find what you're looking for. Answers to all questions can be found at the back of the book, so you can check that you're on the right track.

Instructions

 You **may** use a calculator to answer any question with this symbol.

 You **must not** use a calculator to answer any question with this symbol.

To answer some of the questions in this book, you will need a ruler graduated in centimetres and millimetres, an angle measurer or protractor, a pair of compasses and a calculator. You may also find tracing paper helpful. There is a formulae sheet on the inside front cover of this book. Alternatively, you can download one from www.brookworth.co.uk.

Good luck in your exams!

Contents

Number

Non-Calculator Multiplication
   & Division   4
Fractions & Decimals   5
Negative Numbers   7
Percentages   7
Ratio & Proportion   10
Prime Factorisation   10
Multiples & Factors   11
Powers & Roots   12
Special Numbers   14
Rational, Irrational & Surds   14
Rounding & Estimating   16
Standard Index Form   17

Algebra

Writing & Simplifying Expressions   19
Forming & Solving Equations   19
Substituting Values   21
Rearranging Formulae   22
Algebraic Fractions   23
Straight Lines   25
Simultaneous Equations   27
Inequalities   31
Trial & Improvement   33
Expansion & Factorisation   34
Quadratics   36
Cubic Graphs   40
Travel Graphs   42
Recognising
   & Transforming Graphs   44
Sequences   47
Direct & Inverse Proportion   49

Shape, Space & Measures

Perimeter, Area & Volume   50
Dimensions   53
Plans & Elevations   54
Angles   54
Circle Sectors & Segments   57
Circle Theorems   58
Pythagoras' Theorem   60
Trigonometry   62
3D Trigonometry
   & Pythagoras' Theorem   66
Graphs of
   Trigonometric Functions   67
Similar Shapes   69
Vectors   70
Transformations   72
Converting Between Measures   74
Speed & Density   75
Rounding & Estimating   76
Bearings & Loci   77

Handling Data

Mean, Median, Mode, Range   82
Frequency Tables   83
Frequency Polygons   85
Stem & Leaf Diagrams   87
Moving Averages   88
Cumulative Frequency   89
Box Plots   92
Pie Charts   93
Scatter Graphs   94
Histograms   96
Probability   97
Samples & Surveys   103

Answers   104

Number

N1 A landscape gardener bought 486 garden shrubs, at 62p each, from a local garden centre.

(a) Without using a calculator and showing all your working, work out how much the landscape gardener spent on the shrubs.

Answer £...*(2 marks)*

The garden centre gives its customers an extra shrub free for every 18 bought.

(b) How many extra shrubs did the landscape gardener get?
Show all your working.

Answer...*(2 marks)*

N2 There were 713 runners in a half-marathon race.
Each competitor had to pay 74p towards the cost of the first aid tent.

(a) How much, in total, did the runners contribute towards the first aid tent?

Answer £...*(2 marks)*

NON-CALCULATOR MULTIPLICATION & DIVISION

The organisers of the race were obliged to hire one safety marshal for every 23 competitors.

(b)   How many safety marshals did they have to hire?

Answer..*(2 marks)*

FRACTIONS & DECIMALS

N3   A golf club has 360 members, 24 of whom are junior members. What fraction of members are juniors? Reduce your answer to its lowest terms.

Answer..*(2 marks)*

N4   During November it snowed on five days. On what fraction of days in November did snow fall? Reduce your answer to its lowest terms.

Answer..*(2 marks)*

N5   Find as a fraction in its lowest terms:

(a) $\frac{1}{7} + \frac{2}{35}$

Answer..*(2 marks)*

(b) $\frac{4}{5} - \frac{1}{2}$

Answer..*(2 marks)*

(c) $\frac{3}{10} \div \frac{4}{5}$

Answer..*(2 marks)*   5

Number

FRACTIONS & DECIMALS

 N6 Find as a fraction in its lowest terms:

(a) $\frac{1}{20} + \frac{3}{4}$

Answer ....(2 marks)

(b) $\frac{7}{8} - \frac{1}{4}$

Answer ....(2 marks)

(c) $\frac{3}{11} \times \frac{22}{45}$

Answer ....(2 marks)

 N7 Work out the value of: $1\frac{2}{3} + 2\frac{1}{8}$

Give your answer as a fraction in its simplest form.

Answer ....(3 marks)

 N8 **(a)** Convert 0.15 into a fraction in its lowest terms.

Answer ....(2 marks)

(b) Write down the value of 0.15 × 100.

Answer .... (1 mark)

(c) Write down the value of 0.15 ÷ 100.

Answer .... (1 mark)

(d) What is $(2 - 10) \div (-1 + \frac{3}{4})$?

....

....

....

Answer ....(3 marks)

N9 Write $0.3\dot{1}$ in the form $\frac{a}{b}$, where a and b are positive integers.

....

....

....

....

....

Answer ....*(3 marks)*

N10 Write $0.\dot{4}2\dot{6}$ as a fraction in its simplest form.

....

....

....

....

....

Answer ....*(3 marks)*

N11 Complete these calculations:

(a) $-6 + -4 =$ .... (b) $-6 - -4 =$ ....

(c) $9 \times -3 =$ .... (d) $9 \div -3 =$ .... *(4 marks)*

N12 Complete these calculations:

(a) $-3 + 5 =$ .... (b) $-3 - -5 =$ ....

(c) $-12 \times -3 =$ .... (d) $-12 \div -3 =$ .... *(4 marks)*

N13 A wooden box full of coffee beans weighs 50 kg. The coffee beans themselves weigh 35 kg.

(a) What percentage of the total weight is the weight of the coffee beans?

....

....

Answer .... % *(2 marks)*

(b) What percentage of the total weight is the weight of the wooden box?

....

Answer .... % *(1 mark)*

Number

PERCENTAGES

N14 Red grapes cost £1.90 per kg. White grapes cost 20% more.
How much do white grapes cost?

....

....

....

Answer £...per kg *(3 marks)*

N15 A new car is on sale for £12 000. Given that the car's value will decrease by 15% each year,

(a) how much will the car be worth after 1 year?

....

....

....

Answer £...*(3 marks)*

(b) how much will the car be worth after 2 years?

....

....

....

Answer £...*(3 marks)*

N16 David deposits £400 in a savings account that pays 6% per year compound interest.
If David doesn't make any further deposits or withdrawals, how much money will be in the
account after 2 years?

....

....

....

Answer £...*(3 marks)*

N17 A double glazing manufacturer reduced the price of their most expensive front door from
£620 to £540. What was the percentage reduction in price?
Give your answer to an appropriate degree of accuracy.

....

....

....

Answer .... % *(3 marks)*

N18 Shortly after 25 December, the price of tinsel dropped from £2.10 to £1.60.
What was the percentage reduction in price?
Give your answer to an appropriate degree of accuracy.

....

....

....

Answer .... % *(3 marks)*

N19 A house rose in value by 15% to £72 000 over the last year.

(a) What was the value of the house a year ago?

....

....

....

Answer £ ....*(3 marks)*

The value of a similar house dropped by 5% to £68 000 over the same period.

(b) What was the value of this house a year ago?

....

....

....

Answer £ ....*(3 marks)*

N20 A bottle of vintage wine has risen in value by 10% to £1200 over the last five years.
How much was the bottle of wine worth five years ago?

....

....

....

Answer £ ....*(3 marks)*

N21 The width of a square is increased by 15%. Calculate the percentage change in the area of
the square.

....

....

....

Answer .... % *(3 marks)*

Number

RATIO & PROPORTION

N22 (a) Anthony and Sarah share £55 in the ratio 6 : 4. What is Sarah's share?

....

....

Answer £...*(2 marks)*

(b) What percentage of the money belongs to Anthony?

....

Answer... % *(2 marks)*

N23 John, Tariq and Beth share £45 in the ratio 2 : 3 : 4.
What is John's share?

....

....

....

Answer £...*(3 marks)*

N24 A chocolate cake for 5 people requires 75 g of sugar.
Daphne makes a chocolate cake for 8 people.
Calculate the weight of sugar that Daphne needs.

....

....

Answer...g *(2 marks)*

N25 A pizza for 7 people requires 840 g of flour.
Dennis makes a pizza for 4 people.
Calculate the weight of flour that Dennis needs for his pizza.

....

....

Answer...g *(2 marks)*

PRIME FACTORISATION

N26 (a) The prime factorisation of a certain number is: $2^2 \times 3^2 \times 7$
Write down the number.

Answer... *(1 mark)*

(b) What is the prime factorisation of 90?

....

....

Answer...*(2 marks)*

N27 From the list of numbers 2, 4, 6, 9, 10, 11, write down:

(a) all the multiples of 2,

Answer .... *(1 mark)*

(b) all the factors of 10.

Answer .... *(1 mark)*

x and *y* are two different numbers from the list.

x is a factor of 10, *y* is a multiple of 3 and $x = \frac{5}{3}y$.

(c) Find *x* and *y*.

....

....

....

Answer *x* = ..., *y* = ... *(2 marks)*

N28 **(a)** Find the least common multiple of 12, 21 and 42.

....

....

....

Answer ....(4 marks)*

(b) Find the highest common factor of 12, 16 and 24.

....

....

....

Answer ....*(4 marks)*

N29 Calculate the smallest length of rope that can be cut into an exact number of 4 m lengths, 7 m lengths or 14 m lengths.

....

....

....

....

Answer ....m *(4 marks)*

Number

N30 **(a)** What is the prime factorisation of:

(i) 60?

....

....

Answer ....*(2 marks)*

(ii) 84?

....

....

Answer ....*(2 marks)*

(b) Find the highest common factor of 60 and 84.

....

Answer .... *(1 mark)*

(c) Find the least common multiple of 60 and 84.

....

Answer ....*(2 marks)*

POWERS & ROOTS

N31 Find the value of:

(a) 2^6

....

Answer .... *(1 mark)*

(b) $8^{\frac{2}{3}}$

....

....

Answer ....*(2 marks)*

(c) $9^4 \div 9^2$

....

Answer .... *(1 mark)*

(d) $\dfrac{4^7}{4^3 \times 4^2}$

....

....

Answer ....*(2 marks)*

N32 Find the values of the following numbers, correct to the accuracy given in brackets.

(a) 1.3^6 (3 significant figures)

Answer.. *(1 mark)*

(b) $10^{\frac{1}{5}}$ (2 decimal places)

Answer.. *(1 mark)*

(c) $\left(\frac{4}{3}\right)^{-3}$ (3 significant figures)

Answer.. *(1 mark)*

N33 Work out the following. Show your working and give your answers without indices.

(a) $8^{-\frac{1}{3}}$

....

Answer.. *(1 mark)*

(b) $16^{\frac{1}{4}} \times 32^{\frac{2}{5}}$

....

....

....

Answer..*(3 marks)*

(c) $\dfrac{(5^2)^4}{25^3}$

....

....

Answer..*(2 marks)*

N34 Given that $a^{\frac{5}{2}} \times a^{-3} \times \sqrt{a} = a^y$, find the value of y. Show all your working.

....

....

....

Answer $y =$ ....*(2 marks)*

N35 Find the value of x that satisfies: $4^{-2} \times 2^{-x} = \dfrac{1}{2^6}$

....

....

....

Answer $x =$ ....*(3 marks)*

Number

SPECIAL NUMBERS

N36 Here is a list of numbers: 7, 9, 10, 12, 16, 27

    (a) Which number is a cube number?

        Answer .... *(1 mark)*

    (b) Which two numbers are square numbers?

        Answer ....*(2 marks)*

    (c) Which number is a triangular number?

        Answer ....*(2 marks)*

    (d) From the list, find two numbers x and y such that $\frac{x^2}{3} = y$.

        ....

        ....

        Answer $x = $ ...., $y = $........................*(2 marks)*

N37 x, y and z are different numbers in this list:

$$3, 7, 9, 12, 13, 15, 16$$

x is a triangular number.
y is a prime number.
z is a square number.
$x + y = z$

Work out the values of x, y and z.

    ....

    ....

    ....

    Answer $x = $ ...., $y = $ ...., $z = $ ....*(2 marks)*

RATIONAL, IRRATIONAL & SURDS

N38 Simplify the following, giving your answers in the form $a\sqrt{b}$ where a and b are integers and b is as small as possible.

    (a) $\sqrt{20}$

        ....

        Answer .... *(1 mark)*

    (b) $\sqrt{75} + \sqrt{12}$

        ....

        ....

        Answer ....*(2 marks)*

Rational, Irrational & Surds

N39 **(a)** This list contains rational and irrational numbers: 2π, $1.\dot{2}\dot{3}$, $\frac{5}{7}$, $\sqrt{12}$, $\sqrt{9}$, $\frac{\sqrt{12}}{\sqrt{3}}$
Pick out all the irrational numbers.

Answer ....*(2 marks)*

(b) Find a number that lies between 14 and 15 and has a rational square root.

....

Answer ....*(2 marks)*

(c) Give two different irrational numbers that have a rational product.

....

Answer ....*(2 marks)*

N40 **(a)** Express $\frac{35}{\sqrt{5}}$ in the form $a\sqrt{b}$, where a and b are integers.

Answer ....*(2 marks)*

(b) Simplify this expression:

$\sqrt{2}(9 + \sqrt{2})$

....

....

Answer ....*(2 marks)*

N41 **(a)** Express $\frac{6}{\sqrt{2}}$ in the form $a\sqrt{b}$, where a and b are integers.

Answer ....*(2 marks)*

(b) Simplify the following. Give your answer in the form $p + q\sqrt{3}$, where p and q are integers.

$(2 + \sqrt{3})(4 - \sqrt{3})$

....

....

....

Answer ....*(3 marks)*

Number

ROUNDING & ESTIMATING

N42 Convert the improper fraction $\frac{11}{9}$ to a decimal correct to:

    (a) 3 decimal places,

                           Answer .... *(1 mark)*

    (b) 3 significant figures.

                           Answer .... *(1 mark)*

N43 (a) Estimate the answer to this: $\dfrac{79.6 + 21.8}{32.3 - 9.9}$

                           Answer ....*(2 marks)*

    (b) The entire surface of a sphere of radius 5.2 m is to be painted.
           There is enough paint to cover 280 m².

           Use approximations to estimate whether there is enough paint to cover the sphere.

           ....

           ....

           ....

           ....*(4 marks)*

N44 (a) Estimate the answer to this: $\dfrac{409.2 \times 0.523}{41.6}$

                           Answer ....*(2 marks)*

    (b) The entire surface of the cube shown is to be painted.
           There is enough paint to cover 5000 cm².

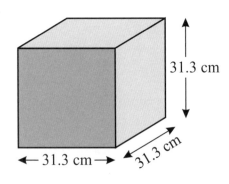

31.3 cm

31.3 cm

31.3 cm

           Use approximations to estimate whether there
           is enough paint.

           ....

           ....

           ....

           ....*(4 marks)*

Number

ROUNDING & ESTIMATING

N45 Calculate, giving your answer to an appropriate degree of accuracy: $\dfrac{29.42 \times 0.0941}{15.2 \times 8.42}$

....

Answer ....*(2 marks)*

N46 Calculate, giving your answer to an appropriate degree of accuracy: $\dfrac{9.59 + 0.024}{7.2 - 1.4}$

....

Answer ....*(2 marks)*

STANDARD INDEX FORM

N47 (a) Write 920 000 in standard form.

Answer .... *(1 mark)*

(b) Write 4.3×10^6 as an ordinary number.

Answer .... *(1 mark)*

N48 Work out the following, giving your answer in standard form.

(a) $(4.1 \times 10^5) + (3.2 \times 10^4)$

....

....

Answer ....*(2 marks)*

(b) $(6.4 \times 10^6) - (3 \times 10^4)$

....

....

Answer ....*(2 marks)*

N49 Work out $(4.8 \times 10^5) \div (2.4 \times 10^{-3})$. Give your answer in standard form.

....

....

....

Answer ....*(3 marks)*

N50 Work out $(3.3 \times 10^{-4}) \times (2 \times 10^7)$. Give your answer in standard form.

....

....

....

Answer ....*(3 marks)*

Number

ROUNDING & ESTIMATING

N45 Calculate, giving your answer to an appropriate degree of accuracy: $\dfrac{29.42 \times 0.0941}{15.2 \times 8.42}$

Answer ....*(2 marks)*

N46 Calculate, giving your answer to an appropriate degree of accuracy: $\dfrac{9.59 + 0.024}{7.2 - 1.4}$

Answer ....*(2 marks)*

STANDARD INDEX FORM

N47 (a) Write 920 000 in standard form.

Answer .... *(1 mark)*

(b) Write 4.3×10^6 as an ordinary number.

Answer .... *(1 mark)*

N48 Work out the following, giving your answer in standard form.

(a) $(4.1 \times 10^5) + (3.2 \times 10^4)$

Answer ....*(2 marks)*

(b) $(6.4 \times 10^6) - (3 \times 10^4)$

Answer ....*(2 marks)*

N49 Work out $(4.8 \times 10^5) \div (2.4 \times 10^{-3})$. Give your answer in standard form.

Answer ....*(3 marks)*

N50 Work out $(3.3 \times 10^{-4}) \times (2 \times 10^7)$. Give your answer in standard form.

Answer ....*(3 marks)*

17

Number

N51 The Moon is 384 000 km from the Earth's surface.

    (a) Write the distance between the Moon and the Earth in standard form.

        Answer.. km *(1 mark)*

The diameter of the Moon is 3.5×10^3 km.

    (b) In terms of the diameter of the Moon, how far is the Moon from the Earth?

    ....

    ....

        Answer.....................................Moon diameters *(2 marks)*

N52 A book contains 6.2×10^2 pages, printed on both sides.

    (a) The thickness of a page is 7.4×10^{-3} cm.
        Disregarding the cover, what is the thickness of the book?

    ....

    ....

        Answer...cm *(2 marks)*

    (b) Without the cover, the book weighs 4.2×10^2 g.
        What is the weight of a single page?

    ....

    ....

        Answer...g *(2 marks)*

N53 The Arctic Ocean has a surface area of 1.4×10^7 km² and an average depth of 1.3×10^3 m.
The Pacific Ocean has a surface area of 1.8×10^8 km² and an average depth of 4.3×10^3 m.

    (a) In terms of surface area, how many times bigger is the Pacific than the Arctic Ocean?

    ....

    ....

        Answer..*(2 marks)*

    (b) On average, how many times deeper is the Pacific Ocean than the Arctic Ocean?

    ....

    ....

        Answer..*(2 marks)*

A1 At a car boot sale, books cost 50 pence and CDs cost 75 pence.
Write an expression in pence for the total cost of x books and y CDs.

....

....

Answer .... pence *(2 marks)*

A2 Simplify the following:

(a) $a^2 \times a^4$

....

Answer .... *(1 mark)*

(b) $5xy^6 \times 2x^3y^2$

....

....

Answer .... *(2 marks)*

(c) $(3x^4y)^3$

....

....

Answer .... *(2 marks)*

A3 Solve the equations:

(a) $\frac{5}{3}x = 2$

Answer $x =$ .... *(1 mark)*

(b) $15 - 3x = 3$

....

....

Answer $x =$ .... *(2 marks)*

(c) $16 - 2x = 4x + 10$

....

....

....

Answer $x =$ .... *(3 marks)*

Algebra

A4 Solve the following equations:

(a) $11 - 6x = -1$

....

....

Answer $x =$ ....*(2 marks)*

(b) $4(2x - 1) = 7x + 11$

....

....

....

Answer $x =$ ....*(3 marks)*

(c) $\dfrac{180}{x + 5} = 9$

....

....

....

Answer $x =$ ....*(3 marks)*

A5 Solve the following equations:

(a) $14 + 9y = 5y + 26$

....

....

....

Answer $y =$ ....*(3 marks)*

(b) $3(5y + 6) = 20y + 8$

....

....

....

Answer $y =$ ....*(3 marks)*

(c) $\dfrac{150}{y + 3} = 10$

....

....

....

Answer $y =$ ....*(3 marks)*

A6 Peri bought 4 books and a bedside lamp from a jumble sale.
The lamp cost £8 and he spent £32 in total.

(a) If each book cost £x, write down an equation in x.

....

....

Answer...*(2 marks)*

(b) Solve your equation to find the cost of one book.

....

....

Answer £...*(2 marks)*

A7 Dan buys 4 jars of garlic and a pot of ground coriander from the supermarket. The pot of coriander weighs 12 g. The whole bag of shopping weighs 852 g.

(a) Write down an equation in y, where y represents the weight of one jar of garlic.

....

....

Answer...*(2 marks)*

(b) Solve the equation for y and hence write down the weight of one jar of garlic.

....

....

Answer ....g *(2 marks)*

A8 If $x = 3$ and $y = 2\frac{1}{2}$, work out the value of:

(a) $2xy$

....

....

Answer...*(2 marks)*

(b) $3x^2 + 2y$

....

....

....

Answer...*(3 marks)*

Algebra

SUBSTITUTING VALUES

A9 Given that $A = 3$ and $B = \frac{2}{3}$, work out the value of:

(a) $\frac{AB}{A^2}$

....

....

....

Answer...*(3 marks)*

(b) $A(B + A)$

....

....

....

Answer...*(3 marks)*

A10 Salespeople are paid according to how many hours they work and the number of products they sell.

(a) If a salesperson receives £6 per hour plus £2 for every item sold, write down a formula for their pay, £P, in terms of hours worked, H, and number of items sold, S.

....

....

Answer $P =$...*(2 marks)*

(b) How much does a salesperson get paid for 37 hours work if 95 items are sold?

....

....

Answer £...*(2 marks)*

REARRANGING FORMULAE

A11 Make a the subject of the formula $b = a^2 + 2$.

....

....

Answer $a =$...*(2 marks)*

A12 Rearrange the formula $4 + 3x = y^{\frac{1}{3}}$, so that x is the subject.

....

....

Answer $x =$...*(2 marks)*

A13 $v^2 = u^2 + 2as$ is a formula used in physics.

(a) Rearrange the formula to give a in terms of u, v and s.

....

....

Answer $a =$..*(2 marks)*

(b) Rearrange the formula to give u in terms of v, a and s.

....

....

Answer $u =$..*(2 marks)*

A14 (a) Express $\dfrac{9x^3 \times 4x^3}{12x^2}$ as simply as possible.

Answer..*(2 marks)*

(b) Combine as a single fraction: $\dfrac{x}{3} + \dfrac{x^2}{6}$

Answer..*(2 marks)*

A15 (a) Express $\dfrac{5x^4 \times 4x^3}{10x^5}$ as simply as possible.

Answer..*(2 marks)*

(b) Simplify: $\dfrac{x^3}{x} - \dfrac{x^2}{2}$

Answer..*(2 marks)*

(c) Solve: $\dfrac{3x}{2} - 6 = \dfrac{x}{2}$

Answer $x =$ ....*(3 marks)*

Algebra

ALGEBRAIC FRACTIONS

 A16 Solve: $1 + \dfrac{2}{x} = 3$

Answer $x = $ ....*(3 marks)*

 A17 (a) Make a the subject of the formula: $b = \dfrac{a+c}{ac}$

Answer $a = $...*(3 marks)*

(b) Write as a single fraction: $\dfrac{4}{x+2} + \dfrac{9}{x-3}$

Answer...*(3 marks)*

 A18 (a) Make x the subject of the equation: $\dfrac{1}{xy} + \dfrac{1}{x} = z$

Answer $x = $...*(3 marks)*

(b) Write as a single fraction: $\dfrac{10}{x+1} - \dfrac{4}{2x+1}$

Answer...*(3 marks)*

A19 (a) At what point does the graph of $y = 2.5 - 0.5x$ cross the y-axis?

Answer (................................, ...) *(1 mark)*

(b) What is the gradient of the graph $y = 2.5 - 0.5x$?

Answer .... *(1 mark)*

(c) Draw the graph of $y = 2.5 - 0.5x$ for values of x between –3 and 3.

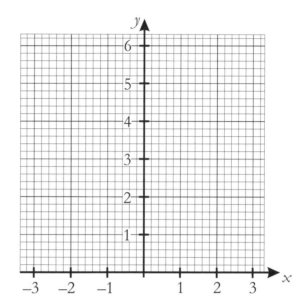

(3 marks)

A20 (a) Draw the graph of $y = \frac{5}{2}x - 2$ for values of x from 0 to 6.

....

....

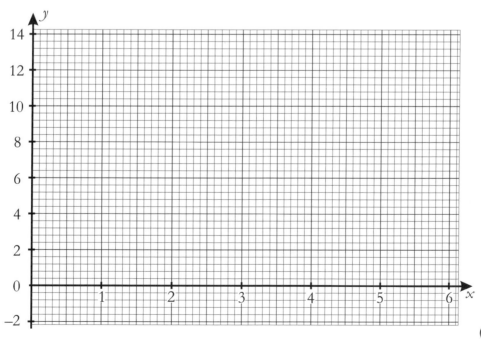

(3 marks)

(b) What is y when $x = 2.8$?   Answer $y =$ .... *(1 mark)*

(c) What is x when $y = 11$?   Answer $x =$ .... *(1 mark)*

Algebra

A21 The cost of hiring a taxi includes a fixed amount and a charge per mile travelled, and is shown in the graph.

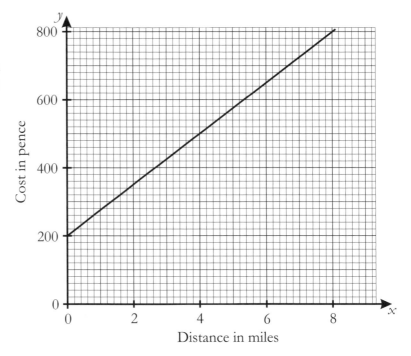

(a) Find the equation of the line in the form $y = ax + b$.

....

....

....

Answer $y =$ ....*(3 marks)*

(b) Calculate the cost of travelling 10 miles in the taxi.

....

Answer £ ....*(2 marks)*

A22 (a) Which of these lines is parallel to the line with equation $2x - 4y = 4$?

$y = 4x - 3$	$3y = 6x - 4$	$y + 4x = 3$
$2y + 4x = 3$	$2 = 2x - y$	$6y = 3x + 8$

....

....

....

Answer ....*(2 marks)*

(b) Which of the lines is perpendicular to the line with equation $x - 2y = 6$?

....

....

....

Answer ....*(2 marks)*

A23 A line passes through the point (4, 9) and is parallel to the line with equation $y = 3x + 1$. Find the equation of the line.

....

....

....

Answer..*(3 marks)*

A24 A line passes through the point (4, 1) and is perpendicular to the line with equation

$y = \frac{1}{4}x - 12$. Find the equation of the line.

....

....

....

Answer..*(3 marks)*

A25 (a) Solve the simultaneous equations: $3x - 5y = 1$
$2x + 3y = 7$

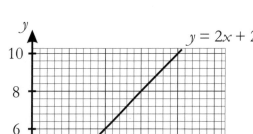

....

....

....

....

....

Answer x = ..., y =..........................*(3 marks)*

(b) The line with equation $y = 2x + 2$
is drawn on the grid.

(i) Draw the line with equation
$y = 10 - 2x$ on the same grid.

(3 marks)

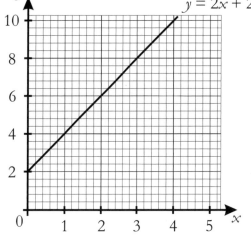

(ii) Write down the value of x where the graphs meet.

Answer x =.. *(1 mark)*

Algebra

A26 **(a)** Find the solution to these simultaneous equations: $4x + 2y = 14$
$x + 3y = 6$

....

....

....

....

....

Answer $x = $ ...., $y = $...........................*(3 marks)*

(b) Draw the graphs of:

(i) $y = 2x$

(ii) $y = 6 - x$

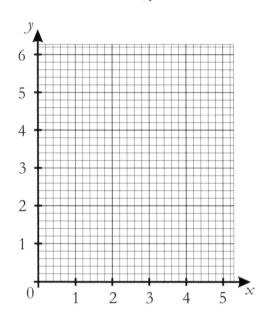

(4 marks)

(iii) Write down the value of y where the graphs meet.

Answer $y = $... *(1 mark)*

A27 Solve these simultaneous equations.
Show all your working.
Do **not** use trial and improvement.

$$4x + 7y = 10$$
$$2x + 3y = 3$$

....

....

....

....

....

Answer $x = $ ...., $y = $...........................*(3 marks)*

A28 Solve these simultaneous equations.
Show all your working.
Do **not** use trial and improvement.

$$9x + 11y = 15$$
$$4x + 4y = 4$$

....

....

....

....

....

Answer $x = $ ...., $y = $ ....*(3 marks)*

A29 (a) Write down the equation of the circle.

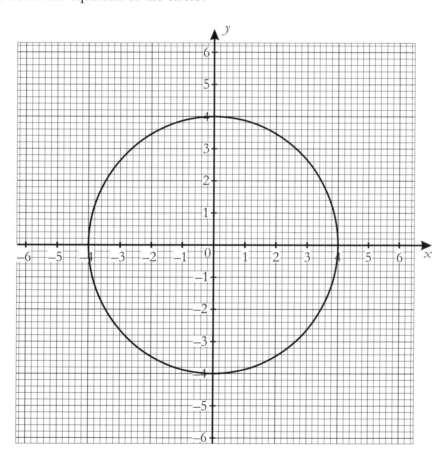

Answer ....*(2 marks)*

(b) By drawing a suitable line on the graph, find the coordinates of the points of
intersection of the circle and the line $y = 4 - x$.

Answer (............, ...), (............, ...) *(2 marks)*

Algebra

SIMULTANEOUS EQUATIONS

A30 Find the coordinates of the points of intersection of the line and circle.

$$y = 5 - \tfrac{1}{3}x$$
$$x^2 + y^2 = 25$$

....

....

....

....

....

....

....

....

....

....

Answer (............, ...), (............, ...) *(7 marks)*

A31 Solve these simultaneous equations.
Show all your working.
Do **not** use trial and improvement.

$$y = 2x - 9$$
$$y = x^2 - 3x - 3$$

....

....

....

....

....

....

....

....

....

....

Answer...*(7 marks)*

A32 List all the possible values of x such that $-5 \leqslant x < 4$, where x is an integer.

Answer...(2 marks)

A33 Write down all the values of x that satisfy $-4 < 2x \leqslant 12$, where x is an integer.

....

....

Answer...(3 marks)

A34 (a) Represent $x < 4$ on the number line below.

$$\begin{array}{cccccccc} | & | & | & | & | & | & | \\ 0 & 1 & 2 & 3 & 4 & 5 & 6 \end{array}$$

(1 mark)

(b) Represent $-1 < x \leqslant 3$ on the number line below.

$$\begin{array}{cccccccc} | & | & | & | & | & | & | \\ -2 & -1 & 0 & 1 & 2 & 3 & 4 \end{array}$$

(2 marks)

A35 (a) Solve the inequality $3(4x + 3) < 15$.

....

....

....

Answer ....(3 marks)

(b) By first drawing three straight lines on the graph paper, shade the region that satisfies $y > 1$, $y \leqslant x$ and $x < 3$.

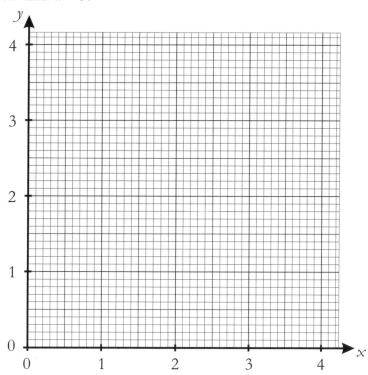

(3 marks)

Algebra

A36 **(a)** Solve the inequality $5(3x - 7) < 5 + 2x$.

....

....

....

....

Answer ....*(3 marks)*

(b) **(i)** Draw the graph of $y + 2x = 6$ for values of x from 0 to 8.

....

....

....

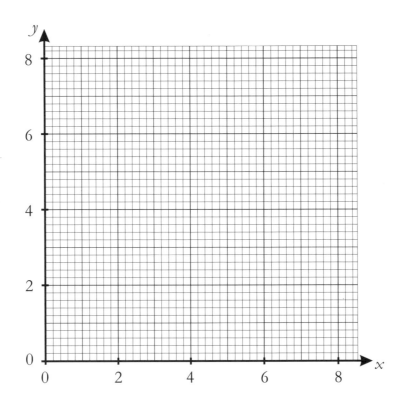

(3 marks)

(ii) Shade the region of points whose coordinates satisfy the four inequalities:

$x < 6$, $y < 5$, $y + 2x \geqslant 6$ and $y > x$. *(2 marks)*

(iii) List the points with whole-number coordinates that satisfy all four inequalities.

Answer .... *(1 mark)*

A37 Ross is using trial and improvement to find a solution to the equation $x^3 + x = 500$.
The table shows his first two trials.

x	$x^3 + x$	Comment
7	350	Too small
8	520	Too big

Continue the table to find a solution to the equation to 1 decimal place.

Answer $x =$ ....*(3 marks)*

A38 The equation

$$x^3 - 5x = 17$$

has a solution between 3 and 4.
Use trial and improvement to find this solution correct to 1 decimal place.

Answer $x =$ ....*(4 marks)*

Algebra

EXPANSION & FACTORISATION

A39 **(a)** Expand and simplify $\quad 3(2m + 5n) - 4n$

....

....

Answer ....*(2 marks)*

(b) Factorise $\quad 9b - 6$

....

Answer .... *(1 mark)*

(c) Factorise fully $\quad 5x^2 - 10x$

....

....

Answer ....*(2 marks)*

A40 **(a)** Expand and simplify $\quad (2x + 9)(x - 7)$

....

....

....

Answer ....*(3 marks)*

(b) Factorise $\quad x^2 + 6x + 8$

....

....

Answer ....*(2 marks)*

A41 **(a)** Expand and simplify $\quad (3x - 2)(5x + 4)$

....

....

....

Answer ....*(3 marks)*

(b) Factorise $\quad 2x^2 + 5x - 3$

....

....

Answer ....*(2 marks)*

A42 Factorise $x^2 - 25y^2$

....

....

Answer ....*(2 marks)*

A43 Factorise $9x^2 - 16y^2$

....

....

Answer ....*(2 marks)*

A44 Complete the square on $x^2 + 6x + 12$.

....

....

....

....

Answer ....*(3 marks)*

A45 $x^2 - 14x + 10$ can be written in the form $(x - a)^2 - b$. Find the values of a and b.

....

....

....

....

Answer $a = $ ...., $b = $ ....*(3 marks)*

A46 Simplify $\dfrac{x^2 - 9y^2}{x - 3y}$

Answer ....*(2 marks)*

A47 Simplify $\dfrac{x^2 + 4x}{x^2 + 3x - 4}$

Answer ....*(3 marks)*

Algebra

A48 **(a)** Factorsise $x^2 + 3x$

....

Answer .... *(1 mark)*

(b) Solve $x^2 + 3x = 0$

....

Answer .... *(1 mark)*

A49 **(a)** Factorsise $x^2 - 4x$

....

Answer .... *(1 mark)*

(b) Solve $x^2 - 4x = 0$

....

Answer .... *(1 mark)*

A50 **(a)** Factorise $x^2 - x - 12$

....

....

Answer ....*(2 marks)*

(b) Solve $x^2 - x - 12 = 0$

....

....

Answer .... *(1 mark)*

A51 **(a)** Factorise $x^2 - 3x - 10$

....

....

Answer ....*(2 marks)*

(b) Solve $x^2 - 3x - 10 = 0$

....

....

Answer .... *(1 mark)*

A52 These two rectangles have the same area:

M _____ N
x cm
P _____ O
$(x + 2)$ cm

A —— B
$(x + 6)$ cm
D — C
1 cm

Not to scale

(a) Form an equation in x and show that it can be simplified to $x^2 + x - 6 = 0$.

....

....

....*(2 marks)*

(b) Solve the equation $x^2 + x - 6 = 0$ to find the length of MP.

....

....

....

....

Answer $MP =$...cm *(4 marks)*

A53 The perimeter of a rectangle is 32 cm and its length is x cm.

(a) Find an expression for the width of the rectangle in terms of x.

....

....

Answer...cm *(2 marks)*

(b) Using the fact that the area of the rectangle is 48 cm², form an equation involving x and show that it can be simplified to $x^2 - 16x + 48 = 0$.

....

....

....*(2 marks)*

(c) Solve the equation $x^2 - 16x + 48 = 0$ to find the two possible lengths of the rectangle.

....

....

....

....

Answer...*(3 marks)*

Algebra

A54 The lengths of the sides of a right-angled triangle are as shown:

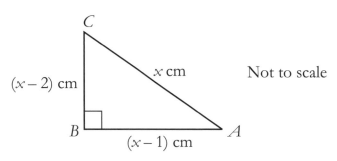

Not to scale

(a) Using Pythagoras' theorem, form and simplify a quadratic equation in x.

....

....

....

....

Answer ....*(4 marks)*

(b) Solve the equation to find an appropriate length for the hypotenuse.

....

....

....

....

Answer ....cm *(4 marks)*

A55 Find the solutions to $3x^2 - 5x + 1 = 0$. Give your answers correct to 2 d.p.

....

....

....

....

Answer ....*(4 marks)*

A56 Find both solutions of $4x^2 + 9x - 2 = 0$. Give your answers to 3 sig. figs.

....

....

....

....

Answer ....*(4 marks)*

A57 (a) Complete the table of values for $y = 4x^2 - 4x - 3$.

x	-2	-1	0	1	2	3
y			-3		5	

(2 marks)

(b) Draw the graph of $y = 4x^2 - 4x - 3$ on the graph paper below.

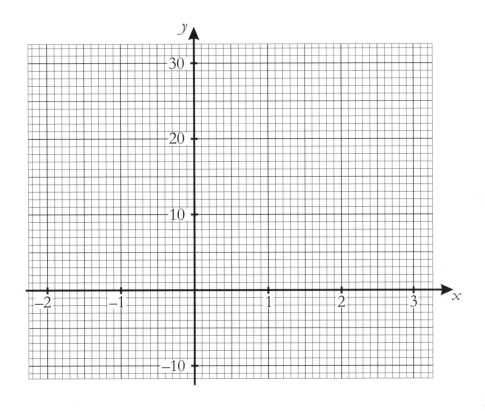

(2 marks)

(c) Use your graph to solve:

(i) $4x^2 - 4x - 3 = 0$

Answer...*(2 marks)*

(ii) $4x^2 - 4x - 3 = 16$

Answer...*(2 marks)*

(d) What is the minimum value of y?

Answer...*(1 mark)*

Algebra

QUADRATICS

A58 (a) Complete the table of values for $y = x^2 - 2x - 1$.

x	−3	−2	−1	0	1	2	3
y	14				−2		2

(2 marks)

(b) Draw the graph of $y = x^2 - 2x - 1$ on the graph paper below.

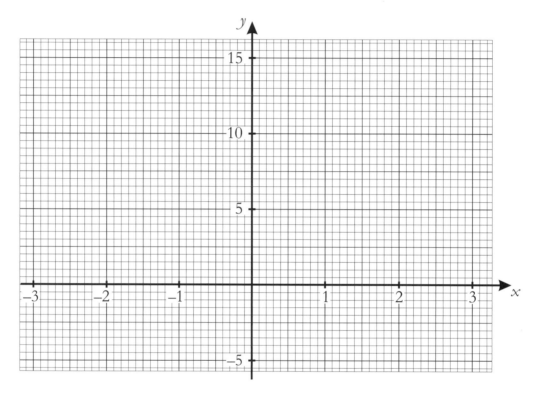

(2 marks)

(c) Use your graph to find the value of y when $x = -2.3$.

Answer.. *(1 mark)*

(d) Solve $x^2 - 2x - 1 = 0$ using your graph.

Answer..*(2 marks)*

CUBIC GRAPHS

A59 (a) Complete the table of values for $y = x^3 + 1$.

x	−3	−2	−1	0	1	2	3
y	−26			1			28

(2 marks)

(b) Draw the graph of $y = x^3 + 1$.

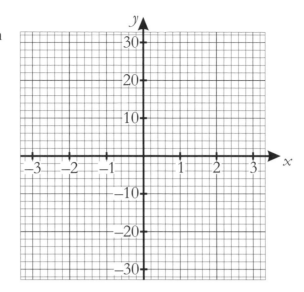

(3 marks)

(c) Use your graph to:

(i) find the value of x when $y = -10$ Answer x = ... *(1 mark)*

(ii) solve $x^3 = 19$

....

Answer x = ... *(2 marks)*

A60 (a) Complete the table of values for $y = -x^3 + 2$.

x	-3	-2	-1	0	1	2	3
y	29			2			-25

(2 marks)

(b) Draw the graph of $y = -x^3 + 2$ for values of x from -3 to 3.

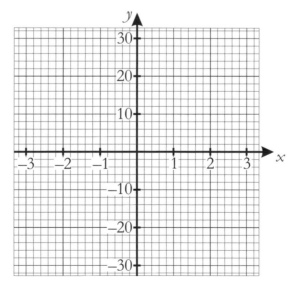

(3 marks)

(c) Use your graph to:

(i) find the value of x when $y = 20$ Answer x = ... *(1 mark)*

(ii) solve $-x^3 + 2 = 0$ Answer x = ... *(1 mark)*

Algebra

A61 The distance–time graph below shows Pippa's journey from her home to her local sports centre. On her way, she takes a parcel to the post office.

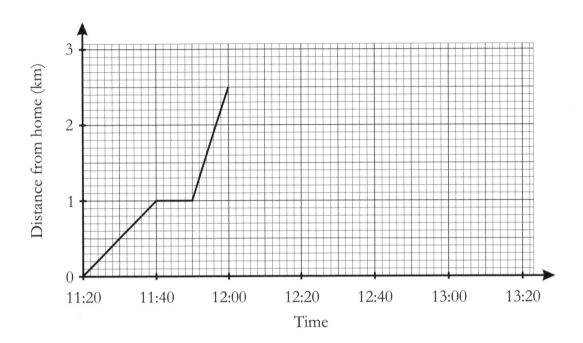

(a) What time did Pippa set off?

Answer... *(1 mark)*

(b) How long was Pippa at the post office?

....

Answer..minutes *(1 mark)*

(c) What is the distance from Pippa's home to the sports centre?

Answer... km *(1 mark)*

Pippa stays at the sports centre until 12:40.
She then travels home at a constant speed, arriving at 13:10.

(d) Complete the travel graph.   *(2 marks)*

(e) Calculate Pippa's speed on the way home.

....

....

Answer... km per hour *(2 marks)*

A62 Pippa and Sarah take part in an 80 m roller-blading race.
Their progress is shown in the graph.

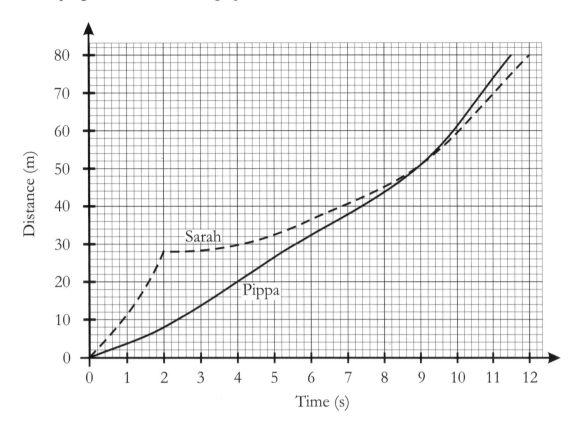

(a) Who won the race?

Answer .... *(1 mark)*

(b) What was the maximum distance between Pippa and Sarah during the race?

Answer .... m *(1 mark)*

(c) What happened to Sarah 2 seconds after the start of the race?

....

.... *(1 mark)*

(d) Who was going the fastest at 9 seconds? Explain.

....

.... *(1 mark)*

Algebra

Travel Graphs

A63 The graph below shows how the speed of a train varies over its journey between stations A and C.

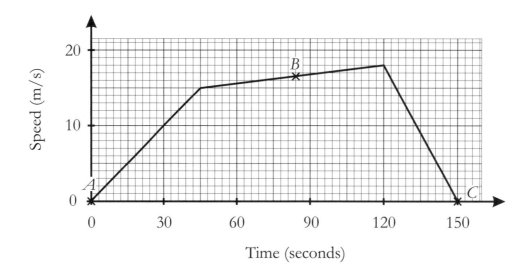

(a) What was the speed of the train at point B?

Answer...m/s *(1 mark)*

(b) What was the acceleration of the train at point B?

....

....

Answer...m/s^2 *(2 marks)*

Recognising & Transforming Graphs

A64 Which of these graphs cannot be $y = x^2 + 2$? Explain.

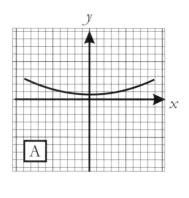
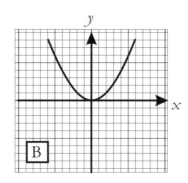
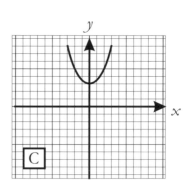

....

....

....*(2 marks)*

A65 Label each graph with its equation.

A: $y = -x^2 + 2$ **B:** $y = \dfrac{1}{x}$ **C:** $y = -x^3$

D: $y = x + 2$ **E:** $y = x^2 - 2$ **F:** $y = x^3$

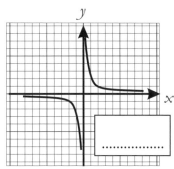
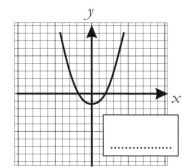
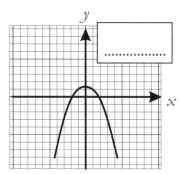

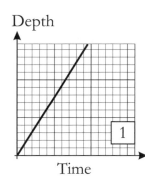
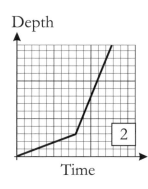
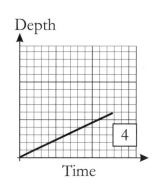

(3 marks)

A66 Water is poured into these odd-shaped vases at a constant rate.
Match each vase to the correct graph.

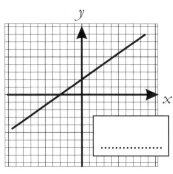

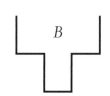
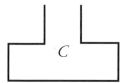

Vase *A* matches graph ....   Vase *B* matches graph ....

Vase *C* matches graph ....   Vase *D* matches graph ....

(3 marks)

Algebra

RECOGNISING & TRANSFORMING GRAPHS

A67 Match the graphs with the statements that follow.

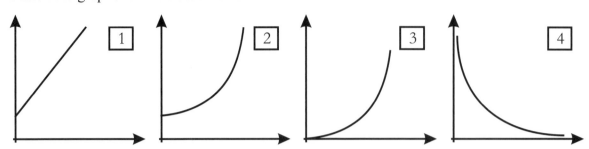

(a) The cost of hiring a taxi per mile including a fixed charge.   Graph ....

(b) $y = \dfrac{1}{x}$ Graph ....

(c) $y = x^3 + 4$ Graph ....

(d) The area of a circle as the radius increases.   Graph ....

(3 marks)

A68 The graph below is $y = f(x)$, where $f(x) = x^2 + x - 6$.

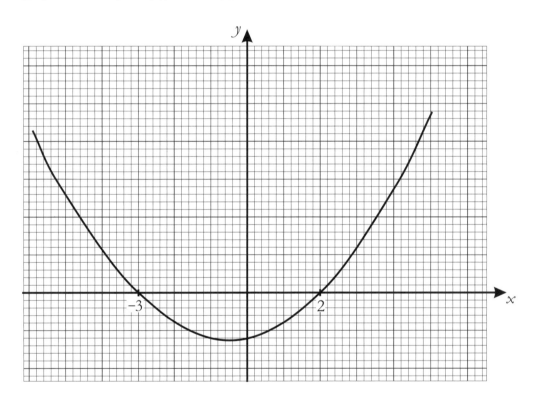

(a) Sketch $y = f(x - 2)$ on the same diagram, labelling the points where the curve cuts the x-axis.

(2 marks)

$y = f(x)$ crosses the y-axis at $y = -6$.

(b) Find the coordinates of the point where the graph of $y = 3f(x)$ crosses the y-axis.

....

Answer (............................, ...) *(2 marks)*

A69 The graph below is $y = f(x)$, where $f(x) = x^3 + 4x^2 - 4x - 16$.

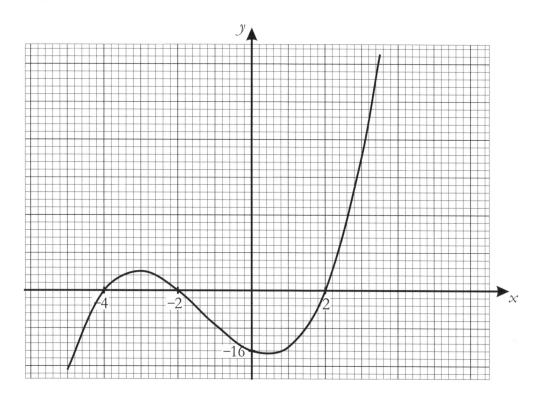

(a) Sketch the graph of $y = f(x) + 10$. Label where the graph cuts the y-axis. *(2 marks)*

(b) The curve $y = f(x)$ is reflected in the y-axis. What is the equation of the new curve?

....

....

Answer $y =$ ....*(2 marks)*

A70 For each of the sequences below, work out an algebraic expression for the nth term.

(a) 2, 7, 12, 17, 22, ...

....

....

....

Answer ....*(2 marks)*

(b) 8, 6, 4, 2, 0, ...

....

....

....

Answer ....*(2 marks)*

Algebra

SEQUENCES

A71 For each of the sequences below, work out an algebraic expression for the *n*th term.

(a) 3, 7, 11, 15, 19, ...

....

....

....

Answer ....*(2 marks)*

(b) 10, 7, 4, 1, –2, ...

....

....

....

Answer ....*(2 marks)*

A72 These are the first three terms of a sequence:

$1 + (2 \times 3), 2 + (3 \times 4), 3 + (4 \times 5), \ldots$

(a) What is the fifth term?

....

Answer .... *(1 mark)*

(b) Work out the *n*th term, simplifying your answer.

....

....

....

Answer ....*(3 marks)*

A73 These are the first three terms of a sequence:

$(1 \times 2)^2, (2 \times 3)^2, (3 \times 4)^2, \ldots$

(a) What is the seventh term?

....

Answer .... *(1 mark)*

(b) Work out the *n*th term of the sequence and simplify your answer.

....

....

....

Answer ....*(3 marks)*

A74 **(a)** *a* is directly proportional to *b*. If *a* = 8 when *b* = 6, work out:

(i) the value of *a* when *b* = 10,

....

....

Answer *a* =...*(2 marks)*

(ii) the value of *b* when *a* = 66.

....

....

Answer *b* =... *(1 mark)*

(b) Given that $y \propto \dfrac{1}{x^2}$ and $x > 0$, complete the table below.

....

....

x	2	5	20	
y	50			2

(3 marks)

A75 **(a)** Given that $q \propto p^2$ and $p > 0$, complete the table below.

....

....

p	2		5	
q	80	180		2000

(3 marks)

(b) The time taken to paint a room is inversely proportional to the number of painters. 3 painters take 2 hours to paint the room.

(i) How long would 9 painters take to paint the room?

....

....

Answer...minutes *(2 marks)*

(ii) If it takes 3 hours to paint the room, how many painters are there?

....

....

Answer...painters *(1 mark)*

Shape, Space & Measures

PERIMETER, AREA & VOLUME

S1 Determine the perimeter of this shape:

4 cm

Not to scale

8 cm

16 cm

4 cm

....

....

Answer...cm *(2 marks)*

S2 A triangular hole is punched out of a rectangular piece of card.

2 cm

4 cm

Not to scale

8 cm

10 cm

Work out the area of the remaining card.

....

....

....

Answer...cm² *(2 marks)*

S3 Calculate the area of this trapezium. State your units.

4.6 m

3.5 m

Not to scale

6.2 m

....

....

Answer... *(2 marks)*

S4 What is the perimeter of the semicircular shape shown? Give your answer to 1 decimal place.

6 cm

Not accurately drawn

....

....

....

Answer...cm *(3 marks)*

S5 Four quarter-circles are intersected with a square to make this shape.

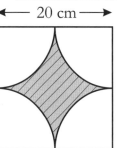

Find the area of the shaded part of the shape.
Leave your answer in terms of π.

....

....

....

....

Answer..cm² *(3 marks)*

S6 **(a)** Calculate the area of this triangle.

5 cm

6 cm

Not to scale

....

Answer.. cm² *(1 mark)*

(b) A triangular prism, based on the triangle above, has a depth of 20 cm.
What is the volume of the triangular prism?

....

....

Answer...cm³ *(2 marks)*

S7 **(a)** Change 8.4 m² to cm².

....

....

Answer...cm² *(2 marks)*

(b) Change 417 cm³ to mm³.

....

....

Answer.. mm³ *(2 marks)*

Shape, Space & Measures

PERIMETER, AREA & VOLUME

S8 Calculate the total surface area of this cylinder.
Leave your answer in terms of π.

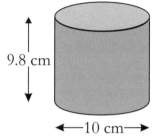

9.8 cm

Not to scale

←10 cm→

....

....

....

....

....

Answer ....cm² *(5 marks)*

S9 Work out the difference in volume between the prism and the cone.

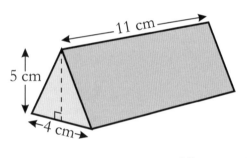

11 cm

5 cm

4 cm

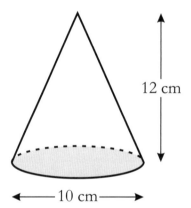

12 cm

10 cm

Not to scale

....

....

....

....

....

Answer ....cm³ *(6 marks)*

S10 The volume of a cylinder is 142.6 cm³. The diameter of the base is 2.6 cm.
Calculate, correct to 3 significant figures, the height of the cylinder.

....

....

....

Answer ....cm *(3 marks)*

S11 This triangular prism has a volume of 132.9 cm³. The length of the prism is 14.2 cm and the width is 3.1 cm.

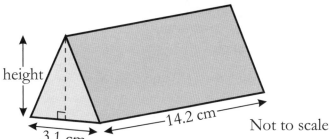

height

3.1 cm

14.2 cm

Not to scale

Calculate the height of the prism, correct to 1 decimal place.

....

....

....

Answer..cm *(3 marks)*

S12 Calculate the volume of a sphere of radius 8 cm.

....

....

....

Answer..cm³ *(3 marks)*

S13 The surface area of a sphere is 3000 cm². Calculate the radius of the sphere.

....

....

....

Answer..cm *(3 marks)*

S14 Steven thinks that the formula for the surface area of a certain solid is:

$$\text{area} = \pi a^2 b, \text{ where } a \text{ and } b \text{ are lengths.}$$

Explain why Steven's formula is wrong.

....

.... *(1 mark)*

S15 Which of the following formulae could be a volume? Give a reason for your answer.

A: $V = \pi r^2 + 4\pi h$ B: $V = r^3 + r^2h + rh$

C: $V = \pi r^2 h^2$ D: $V = 4rh^2 + r^3$

Formula .... because ....

.... *(2 marks)*

Shape, Space & Measures

S16 The drawing shows a cuboid with a triangular prism removed.
All measurements are in centimetres.

Draw full size front (*F*) and side (*S*) elevations on the grid below.

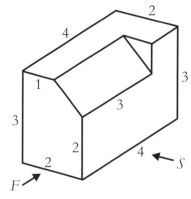

Not to scale

Front elevation (*F*)					Side elevation (*S*)				

(4 marks)

ANGLES

S17 (a) Explain why angle *x* is 60°.

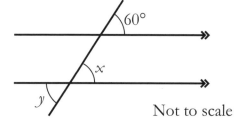

Not to scale

....

.... *(1 mark)*

(b) Write down the size of angle *y*.   Answer *y* = ... degrees *(1 mark)*

S18 (a) Explain why angle *a* is 50°.

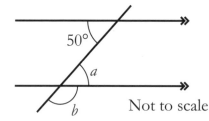

Not to scale

....

.... *(1 mark)*

(b) What is the size of angle *b*?

....

Answer *y* = ... degrees *(1 mark)*

Shape, Space & Measures

S19 **(a)** Explain why angle *x* is 60°.

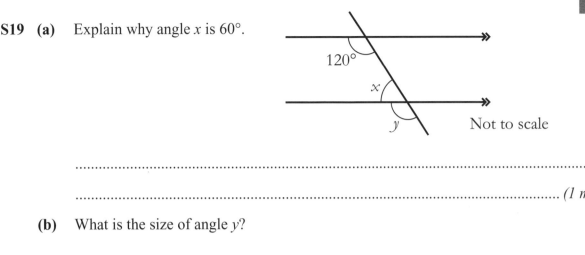

120°

x

y

Not to scale

....

.... *(1 mark)*

(b) What is the size of angle *y*?

....

Answer *y* = ... degrees *(1 mark)*

S20 **(a)** Explain why angle *a* is 320°.

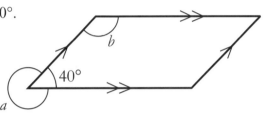

b

40°

a

Not to scale

....

.... *(1 mark)*

(b) What is the size of angle *b*?

....

Answer *b* = ... degrees *(1 mark)*

S21 **(a)** Calculate the sum of the interior angles of a hexagon.

....

....

Answer ....degrees *(2 marks)*

(b) Work out the size of the angles marked *x*.

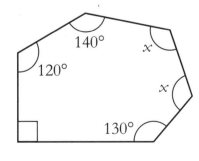

140°

x

120°

x

130°

Not to scale

....

....

Answer *x* = ...degrees *(2 marks)*

55

Shape, Space & Measures

ANGLES

S22 Using the diagram below, find the size of the angles marked x.

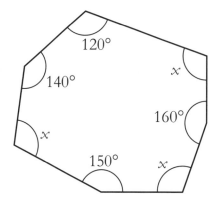

Not to scale

....

....

....

....

Answer $x =$ ....degrees *(4 marks)*

S23 In the quadrilateral *ABCD*, angle *ABC* = 90°, angle *CDA* = 90°, angle *BCD* = 60° and *BC* = *CD*.

(a) Draw a rough sketch of the quadrilateral *ABCD*.

(3 marks)

(b) Find the size of angle *BAD*.

....

Answer .... degrees *(1 mark)*

S24 The diagram shows a circle of radius 5 cm with centre at *O*.
The angle at the centre of sector *AOB* is 30°.

Not to scale

O

30°

5 cm

A

B

(a) What is the circumference of the circle?

....

....

Answer...cm *(2 marks)*

(b) What is the length of the arc *AB*?

....

Answer... cm *(1 mark)*

(c) What is the area of the shaded sector, *AOB*?

....

....

....

Answer...cm² *(3 marks)*

S25 What is the perimeter of the shaded
shape, cut from a circle centred at *O*?

3 cm

O

Not to scale

2 cm

....

....

....

....

Answer...cm *(4 marks)*

Shape, Space & Measures

CIRCLE SECTORS & SEGMENTS

S26 An equilateral triangle, *XYZ*, is circumscribed by a circle with centre *O*. The circumference of the circle is 60 cm.

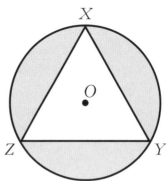

(a) Calculate the radius of the circle.

....

....

Answer...cm *(2 marks)*

(b) Write down the size of angle *XYZ*.

Answer...degrees *(1 mark)*

(c) Work out the shaded area.

....

....

....

....

Answer...cm² *(5 marks)*

CIRCLE THEOREMS

S27 Angle *AOC* = 76°, where *O* is the centre of the circle.

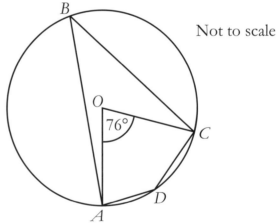

Not to scale

(a) Find the size of angle *ABC*.

....

Answer...degrees *(1 mark)*

(b) Find the size of angle *ADC*.

....

Answer...degrees *(1 mark)*

S28 *TA* and *TB* are tangents from *T* to the circle with centre *O*.
Angle *ATB* = 36°.

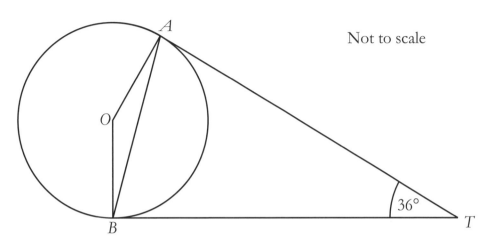

Not to scale

(a) Find the size of angle *BAT*.

....

Answer ....degrees *(2 marks)*

(b) Find the size of angle *OAB*.

....

Answer ....degrees *(2 marks)*

S29 *O* is the centre of the circle.
The line segment *AC* passes through *O*.
Angle *ACB* = 38°.

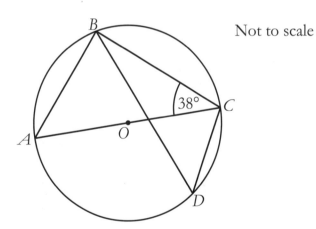

Not to scale

(a) Find the size of angle *BAC*.

....

Answer ....degrees *(2 marks)*

(b) Write down the size of angle *BDC*.
Give a reason for your answer.

Angle *BDC* = ... degrees

Reason: ....

....*(2 marks)*

Shape, Space & Measures

CIRCLE THEOREMS

S30 Angle $ACD = 58°$.
AC passes through the centre of the circle, O.
CP is a tangent to the circle and AP passes through D.

Not to scale

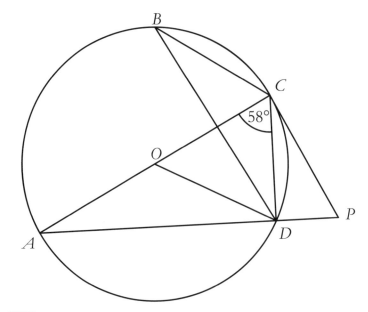

(a) Calculate the size of angle CBD.

....

....

....

....

Answer..degrees *(4 marks)*

(b) Calculate the size of angle CPA.

....

....

....

....

Answer..degrees *(3 marks)*

PYTHAGORAS' THEOREM

S31 Find the length AB.
Give your answer to 1 d.p.

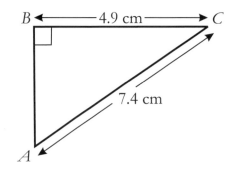

Not to scale

....

....

....

Answer..cm *(3 marks)*

S32 Use Pythagoras' theorem to find the length *AD*.

B

7.4 cm

4.9 cm

A

C

6.3 cm

D

Not to scale

....

....

....

....

....

....

Answer ....cm *(5 marks)*

S33 Desmond runs 1500 m due east, then 800 m due north and then 600 m due west.
Calculate how far, in a straight line, Desmond is from his starting point.
It may be helpful to start by sketching a rough diagram.

Answer ....m *(4 marks)*

Shape, Space & Measures

PYTHAGORAS' THEOREM

S34 The line segment *AB* goes
from *A* (2, 3) to *B* (5, −1).

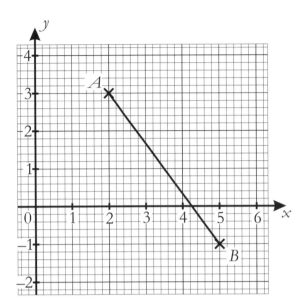

(a) Work out the coordinates
of the mid-point of *AB*.

....

....

....

Answer (..........................., ...) *(3 marks)*

(b) Work out the length of *AB*.

....

....

....

Answer ....units *(3 marks)*

TRIGONOMETRY

S35

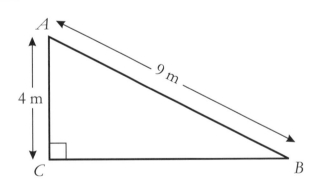

Not to scale

Calculate the angle *ABC*.

....

....

....

Answer ....degrees *(3 marks)*

S36

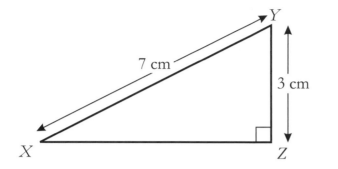

Not to scale

Find the size of angle *XYZ*.

....

....

....

Answer...degrees *(3 marks)*

S37 In the diagram, *WX* = 5 m, *ZY* = 3 m and angle *XWZ* = 40°.

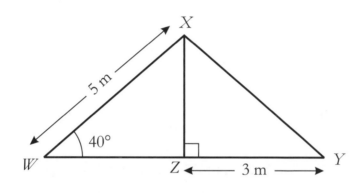

Not to scale

(a) Calculate the length *XZ*.

....

....

....

Answer...m *(3 marks)*

(b) Calculate angle *ZXY*.

....

....

....

Answer...degrees *(3 marks)*

Shape, Space & Measures

S38

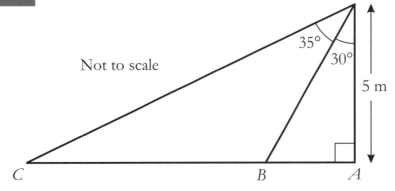

Not to scale

Length $AD = 5$ m, angle $ADB = 30°$ and angle $CDB = 35°$.

(a) Calculate the length AB.

....

....

....

Answer..m *(3 marks)*

(b) Calculate the length BC.

....

....

....

Answer..m *(3 marks)*

S39 A tree AB is 15 m high. Point C is 52 m from B, the base of the tree, on level ground.

(a) Sketch a rough diagram to show this information.

(2 marks)

(b) What is the angle of elevation of A from C?

....

....

....

Answer...degrees *(3 marks)*

S40 The diagram shows triangle *ABC*:
AB = 75 cm, *AC* = 40 cm
Angle *BAC* = 26°

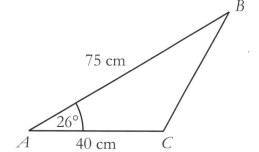

Not to scale

(a) Calculate the area of the triangle.
Give your answer correct to 3 significant figures.

....

....

Answer ....cm² *(2 marks)*

(b) Calculate the length of *BC*.
Give your answer correct to 3 significant figures.

....

....

....

Answer ....cm *(3 marks)*

S41 The diagram shows triangle *XYZ*:
XZ = 19 m, *YZ* = 38 m
Angle *XYZ* = 28°

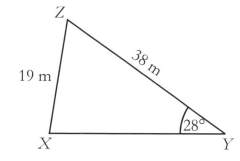

Not to scale

(a) Calculate the size of angle *YXZ* to the nearest degree.

....

....

....

Answer ....degrees *(3 marks)*

(b) Calculate the area of the triangle.
Give your answer correct to 3 significant figures.

....

....

....

Answer ....cm² *(3 marks)*

Shape, Space & Measures

3D TRIGONOMETRY & PYTHAGORAS' THEOREM

S42 In this square-based pyramid,
E is vertically above F,
the midpoint of AC.
AB = 20 cm and EC = 40 cm.

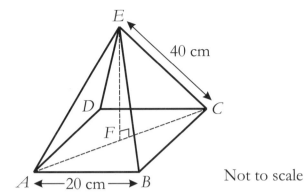

40 cm

Not to scale

(a) Calculate the length AF.

....

....

Answer..cm *(2 marks)*

(b) Find the angle between EC and the base ABCD.

....

....

....

Answer..degrees *(3 marks)*

(c) Calculate the height of the pyramid EF.

....

....

....

Answer..cm *(3 marks)*

S43 In this triangular prism,
F is vertically above G,
the midpoint of AB.
AB = 4 cm and BC = 10 cm.

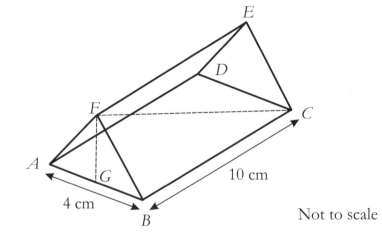

10 cm

4 cm

Not to scale

(a) Given that angle AFB = 40°, write down the size of angle FAB.

Answer... degrees *(1 mark)*

3D TRIGONOMETRY & PYTHAGORAS' THEOREM

(b) Work out the height of the triangular prism, *FG*.

....

....

....

Answer...cm *(3 marks)*

(c) Work out the length *FC*.

....

....

....

....

Answer...cm *(4 marks)*

GRAPHS OF TRIGONOMETRIC FUNCTIONS

S44 The graph shows $y = \sin(x)$, $0° \leqslant x \leqslant 360°$.

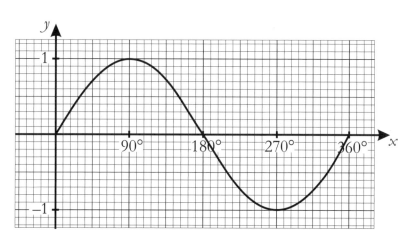

(a) Clearly show on the graph how you would find solutions to $\sin(x) = -0.5$ for $0° \leqslant x \leqslant 360°$.

(1 mark)

(b) Use your calculator to work out these solutions.

....

....

Answer...*(2 marks)*

Shape, Space & Measures

GRAPHS OF TRIGONOMETRIC FUNCTIONS

S45

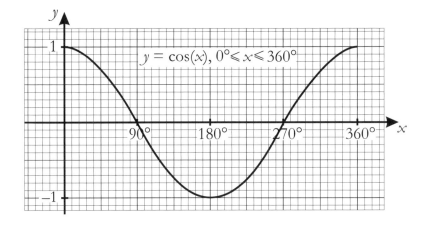

Use your calculator and the graph to find all the solutions of cos(x) = 0.2, for values of x between 0° and 360°. Give your answers correct to 2 d.p.

....

....

....

Answer ....*(3 marks)*

S46 **(a)** Without drawing a table of values, sketch the graph of y = tan(2x) for values of x from −180° to 180°.

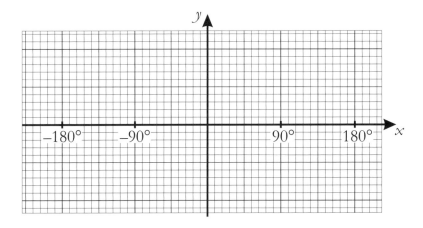

(2 marks)

(b) Using your graph, find all the solutions to tan(2x) = 0 for values of x between −180° and 180° inclusive.

Answer .... *(1 mark)*

S47

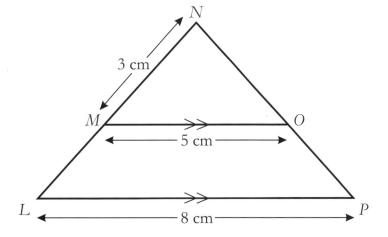

Not to scale

$LP = 8$ cm, $MO = 5$ cm, $MN = 3$ cm and LP is parallel to MO.
Calculate the length LN.

....

....

....

Answer ....cm *(3 marks)*

S48

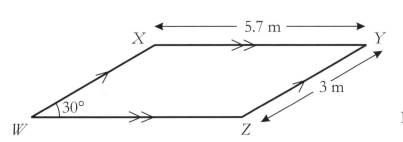

Not to scale

The parallelogram above is enlarged so that XY becomes 8.2 m.

(a) Calculate the new length of the side ZY.

....

....

....

Answer ....m *(2 marks)*

(b) What is the size of angle WXY in the enlarged parallelogram?

....

....

Answer .... degrees *(1 mark)*

Shape, Space & Measures

S49 $\mathbf{a} = \begin{pmatrix} 4 \\ 3 \end{pmatrix}$, $\mathbf{b} = \begin{pmatrix} 2 \\ -1 \end{pmatrix}$

(a) Work out, as a column vector, $\mathbf{a} + \mathbf{b}$.

....

Answer .... *(1 mark)*

(b) What is $2\mathbf{a} - \mathbf{b}$?

....

Answer .... *(1 mark)*

S50 $\mathbf{x} = \begin{pmatrix} -2 \\ -1 \end{pmatrix}$, $\mathbf{y} = \begin{pmatrix} 3 \\ -4 \end{pmatrix}$

(a) Work out, as a column vector, $\mathbf{x} - \mathbf{y}$.

....

Answer .... *(1 mark)*

(b) What is $2\mathbf{y} - 3\mathbf{x}$?

....

Answer .... *(1 mark)*

S51 $\overrightarrow{AB} = \mathbf{a}$, $\overrightarrow{AC} = \mathbf{b}$, $\overrightarrow{BD} = \mathbf{c}$ and *ABCD* is a quadrilateral.

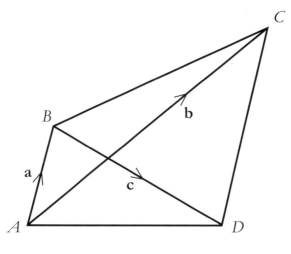

Not to scale

(a) Write down, in terms of **a**, **b** and **c**, the vectors:

(i) $\overrightarrow{AD}$ Answer .... *(1 mark)*

(ii) $\overrightarrow{CB}$ Answer .... *(2 marks)*

(b) Given that $\overrightarrow{DC}$ = 2**a**, find an expression for **a** in terms of **b** and **c**.

....

....

....

Answer **a** =...*(3 marks)*

S52 *WXYZ* is a cyclic quadrilateral, with *O* the centre of the circle.

$\overrightarrow{WZ}$ = **a**, $\overrightarrow{OW}$ = **b** and $\overrightarrow{OY}$ = **c**.

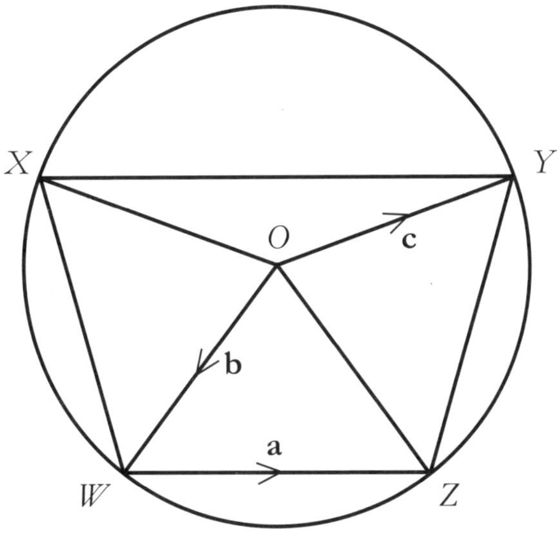

Not to scale

(a) Find, in terms of **a**, **b** and **c**:

(i) $\overrightarrow{OZ}$

Answer.. *(1 mark)*

(ii) $\overrightarrow{ZY}$

Answer...*(2 marks)*

(b) Given that the chord *XY* is twice as long and parallel to the chord *WZ*, find an expression for *XW* in terms of **a**, **b** and **c**.

....

....

....

Answer...*(3 marks)*

Shape, Space & Measures

S53 The diagram shows the positions of three shapes, *L*, *M* and *N*.

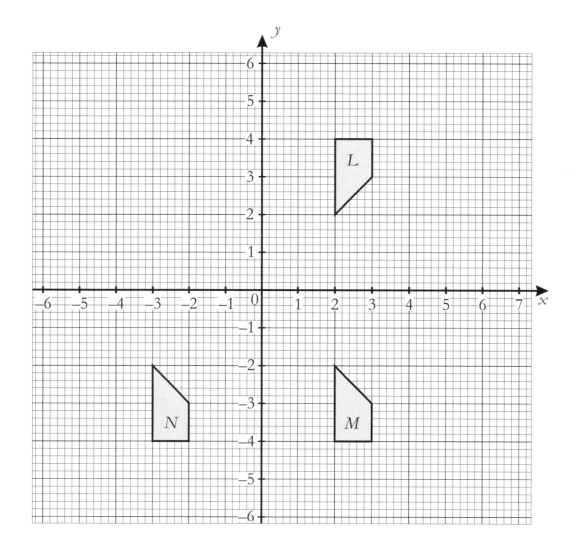

(a) Describe the transformation that moves *L* onto *M*.

....

....*(2 marks)*

(b) Describe the transformation that moves *M* onto *N*.

....

....*(2 marks)*

S54   The diagram shows the positions of three shapes *A*, *B* and *C*.

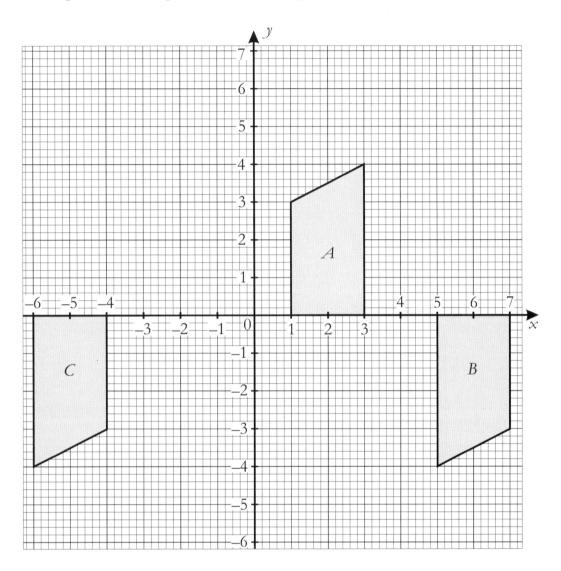

(a)   Describe a single transformation that takes *A* onto *B*.

....

....*(2 marks)*

Shape *A* is reflected in the *y*-axis.

(b)   Draw the new position of *A*. Label it *D*.   *(1 mark)*

(c)   Describe a sequence of transformations which take *D* onto *C*.

....

....

....

....*(4 marks)*

Shape, Space & Measures

TRANSFORMATIONS

S55

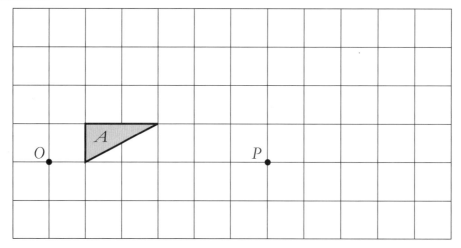

(a) Enlarge triangle *A* by a scale factor of 3 with centre of enlargement *O*.
Label the enlarged triangle *B*. *(2 marks)*

(b) Draw the enlargement of triangle *B* with scale factor $-\frac{1}{3}$ and centre *P*. *(2 marks)*

S56 Shape *A* is enlarged to obtain shape *B*.

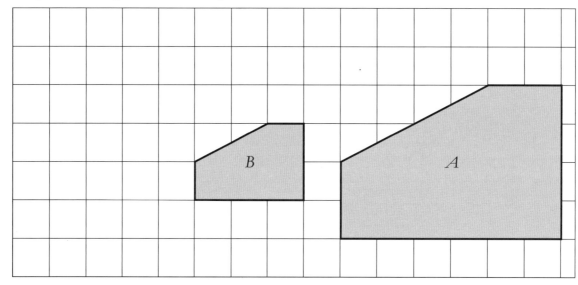

(a) What is the scale factor of the enlargement?

....

Answer.. *(1 mark)*

(b) Mark with a cross the centre of enlargement for the transformation. *(1 mark)*

CONVERTING BETWEEN MEASURES

S57 Given that 1 mile is approximately 1.6 km, which distance is the greater: 15 miles or 25 000 metres?

....

....

Answer..*(2 marks)*

Shape, Space & Measures

CONVERTING BETWEEN MEASURES

S58   Which is the heavier, 110 pounds or 47 000 g?
(1 kilogram is approximately equal to 2.2 lbs)

....

....

Answer ....(2 marks)

SPEED & DENSITY

S59   I once ran the 400 m in 48.6 seconds.
What was my average speed in metres per second?

....

....

Answer .... m/s (2 marks)

S60   A car travelled 182 miles in 3.5 hours.
What was the average speed in miles per hour?

....

....

Answer ....mph (2 marks)

S61   A man ran at an average speed of 3.2 m/s for 8 minutes. How many kilometres did he travel?

....

....

....

Answer ....km (3 marks)

S62   A piece of metal has a mass of 5000 kg and a volume of 1.2 m^3.
Calculate the density of the metal.

....

....

Answer .... kg/m^3 (2 marks)

S63   A sample of soil taken from a field has a density of 200 kg/m^3.
25 tonnes of soil is to be removed from the field in order to turn it into a golf course.
What volume of soil will be removed from the field?

....

....

....

Answer .... m^3 (3 marks)

Shape, Space & Measures

ROUNDING & ESTIMATING

S64 A vet weighed a dog on scales that were accurate to the nearest 10 g.
The display showed the dog's weight as 32.49 kg.

(a) What is the maximum that the dog could have weighed?

....

Answer.. kg *(1 mark)*

(b) What is the minimum that the dog could have weighed?

....

Answer.. kg *(1 mark)*

S65 A javelin was thrown 52.4 m to the nearest 10 cm.

(a) What is the maximum distance that the javelin could have been thrown?

....

Answer.. m *(1 mark)*

(b) What is the minimum distance that the javelin could have been thrown?

....

Answer.. m *(1 mark)*

S66 *ABCD* is a rectangle of length 7.2 cm and width 4.5 cm, both correct to 1 decimal place.

A B

4.5 cm

Not to scale

D 7.2 cm C

Calculate the upper bound and the lower bound for the area of the rectangle *ABCD*.

....

....

....

....

....

Upper bound = ... cm^2

Lower bound =... cm^2 *(5 marks)*

ROUNDING & ESTIMATING

S67 (a) The radius of a cone is given by the formula $r = \frac{A}{\pi l}$.

If $A = 4.65$ cm^2 correct to 2 decimal places and $l = 2.5$ cm correct to 1 decimal place, work out the upper bound for the radius of the cone.
Give your answer to 4 significant figures.

....

....

....

Answer...cm *(3 marks)*

(b) The formula for the volume of a cone is $V = \frac{1}{3}\pi r^2 h$.

If $r = 9.58$ cm and $h = 2.43$ cm, both correct to 2 decimal places, work out the lower bound for the volume of the cone. Give your answer to 4 significant figures.

....

....

....

Answer...cm^3 *(3 marks)*

BEARINGS & LOCI

S68 Below is a map of an island.

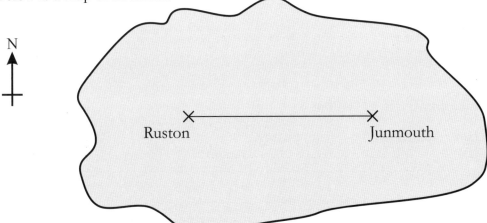

The scale of the map is 1 : 40 000.

(a) What is the distance between Ruston and Junmouth in metres?

....

....

Answer...m *(2 marks)*

Marham is on a bearing of 030° from Ruston and a bearing of 300° from Junmouth.

(b) Mark on the map the position of Marham. *(3 marks)*

Shape, Space & Measures

S69 Below is a scale drawing of two boats at sea.
Boat Q is due south of boat P.

The scale of the drawing is 1 : 10 000.

(a) How far in real life is boat P from boat Q?

....

....

Answer...m *(2 marks)*

(b) Mark on the diagram the position of boat R, which is 1000 m from P on a bearing of 120°.

....

....*(3 marks)*

S70 The diagram shows the positions of three buoys: *A*, *B* and *C*.

A

B

C

(a) What is the bearing of *B* from *A*?

Answer .... *(1 mark)*

A racing yacht is anchored:

    (i) along the bisector of angle *ABC*;

    (ii) along the bisector of angle *ACB*.

(b) By drawing the loci of **(i)** and **(ii)** mark clearly the position of the yacht. *(4 marks)*

Shape, Space & Measures

BEARINGS & LOCI

S71 The diagram shows the positions of two electricity pylons, *X* and *Y*.
David is standing at *Z*.

Scale: 1 cm to 1 km

(a) What is the bearing of *Y* from *X* ?

Answer .... *(1 mark)*

(b) What is the actual distance of *Y* from *Z* ?

....

Answer .... km *(1 mark)*

David can see his friend Rupinder at *A*. Rupinder is further north than David.
Rupinder is equidistant from *X* and *Y* and is 5 km from David.

(c) Mark the position of *A* with a cross. *(3 marks)*

S72 Below is a scale drawing of an outdoor triangular-shaped swimming pool. The scale is 1 cm to 5 m.

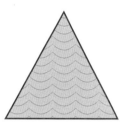

To stop grass growing within 12 m of the pool some organic weedkiller is to be sprayed next to the pool.

Shade on the diagram the area in which the weedkiller should be sprayed. *(3 marks)*

S73

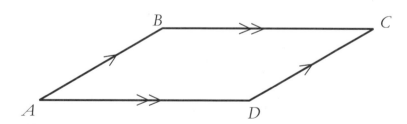

Draw accurately the locus of points that are 2 cm from the edge of the parallelogram *ABCD*. *(2 marks)*

Handling Data

H1 **(a)** Sakina measures the diameters of some beef tomatoes.
The diameters, in mm, are:

$$80, 82, 82, 83, 85, 89, 91, 92, 92, 94$$

(i) What is the range of the diameters of the beef tomatoes?

....

Answer...mm *(1 mark)*

(ii) What is the mean diameter of the beef tomatoes?

....

....

....

Answer...mm *(3 marks)*

To compare, Sakina measures the diameters of some plum tomatoes.
The range of these diameters is 18 mm and the mean 62 mm.

(b) Use the range and mean to compare these two varieties.

....

....

....*(2 marks)*

H2 The weights of 9 badminton players are shown below.

75 kg, 81 kg, 74 kg, 84 kg, 74 kg, 78 kg, 83 kg, 74 kg, 83 kg

(a) Find their median weight.

....

....

Answer...kg *(2 marks)*

(b) Find the mode of their weights.

Answer...kg *(1 mark)*

(c) Which of **(a)** and **(b)** is not a good indicator of their average weight? Why?

....

.... *(1 mark)*

Handling Data

MEAN, MEDIAN, MODE, RANGE

H3 Luke carried out a survey of how much money 8 of his friends had deposited in their savings accounts. The amounts were £47, £55, £63, £57, £82, £4002, £55 and £12.

(a) What was the mean amount deposited?

....

....

....

Answer £..*(3 marks)*

(b) Find the median.

....

....

Answer £..*(2 marks)*

(c) Look at your answers to **(a)** and **(b)**. Which does not give a good indication of the average savings of the 8 friends? Explain your answer.

....

.... *(1 mark)*

FREQUENCY TABLES

H4 The frequency table below shows the number of goals scored by 40 non-league football teams one Saturday afternoon.

Number of Goals	Number of Teams
0	11
1	13
2	9
3	5
4	2

(a) Calculate the mean number of goals per team.

....

....

....

Answer..*(4 marks)*

(b) What is the modal number of goals scored per team?

Answer.. *(1 mark)*

Handling Data

H5 The table below shows the number of eggs laid by 100 different hens.

Number of Eggs	Number of Hens
0	18
1	32
2	26
3	12
4	8
5	4

(a) Calculate the mean number of eggs laid per hen.

....

....

....

Answer...*(4 marks)*

(b) What is the modal number of eggs laid?

Answer.. *(1 mark)*

(c) What is the median number of eggs laid?

....

....

Answer.. *(2 marks)*

H6 Joe carried out a survey to find out how long people spent cleaning their teeth in the morning.

Time (*t* seconds)	Number
$0 < t \leqslant 20$	4
$20 < t \leqslant 40$	17
$40 < t \leqslant 60$	15
$60 < t \leqslant 80$	10
$80 < t \leqslant 100$	3

(a) Which class contains the median? Explain how you found your answer.

Class ....

because ....

....*(2 marks)*

(b) Write down the modal class.

Answer.. *(1 mark)*

(c) Estimate the mean time these people spent cleaning their teeth.
Give your answer to the nearest second.

....

....

....

Answer... seconds *(4 marks)*

H7 The deputy manager of a garden centre measured the heights of 24 rose bushes.
Below is his data in cm.

52	54	59	43	50	51	52	53	49	47	46	53
49	42	58	56	44	52	48	51	49	47	46	53

(a) Complete the grouped frequency table for the heights of the rose bushes.

Height (h cm)	Tally	Frequency
$40 \leqslant h < 44$		
$44 \leqslant h < 48$		
$48 \leqslant h < 52$		
$52 \leqslant h < 56$		
$56 \leqslant h < 60$		

(3 marks)

(b) Draw a frequency polygon to represent the data.

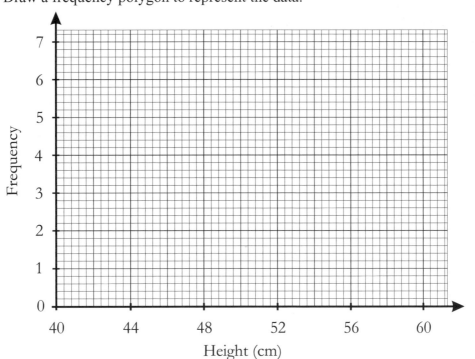

(3 marks)

85

Handling Data

H8 Geoff timed how long his racing pigeons took to return home after being released some distance away. His data, in minutes, is recorded below.

43	30	50	55	46	37	52	47	41	49
53	44	49	43	50	41	59	45	48	47
47	40	45	58	33	34	42	49	36	43

(a) Complete the grouped frequency table for the times.

Time (*T* mins)	Tally	Frequency
$30 \leqslant T < 36$		
$36 \leqslant T < 42$		
$42 \leqslant T < 48$		
$48 \leqslant T < 54$		
$54 \leqslant T < 60$		

(3 marks)

(b) Draw the frequency polygon for the times on the graph paper below.

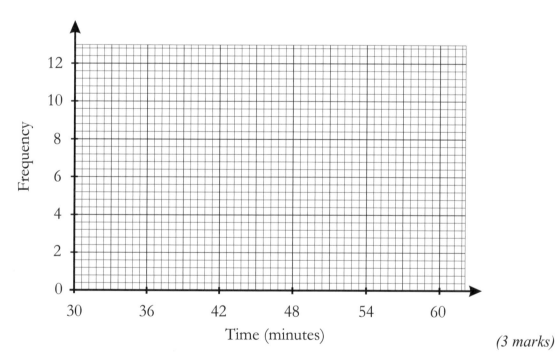

Time (minutes)

(3 marks)

86

H9 These are the marks obtained by 20 pupils in a science test.

13 42 34 20 24 42 26 29 30 49
33 14 36 38 23 26 42 46 48 31

(a) Show this information in an ordered stem and leaf diagram.

```
1 |
2 |
3 |
4 |
```

Key 3|4 represents a mark of 34

(3 marks)

(b) What is the mode for the data?

Answer .... *(1 mark)*

(c) What is the median?

....

....

Answer .... *(2 marks)*

H10 Below are the number of shots taken by 24 golfers in the final round of a tournament.

64 87 67 68 95 91 70 83 72 71 73 90
72 64 72 71 65 72 68 81 70 87 69 89

(a) Draw an ordered stem and leaf diagram for the data.

```
  |
——+——————————————
  |
——+——————————————
  |
——+——————————————
  |
```

Key 6|7 represents 67 shots

(3 marks)

(b) The median of the scores in the final round is to become the new par for the course.
What is the new par for the course?

....

....

Answer .... *(2 marks)*

Handling Data

MOVING AVERAGES

H11 The table shows the number of employees working for a walking boot manufacturer over a three-year period.

	March	June	September	December
2004	68	78	72	42
2005	62	72	75	38
2006	57	64	68	36

(a) Plot the data as a time series on the graph paper.
The data for 2004 has been plotted for you.

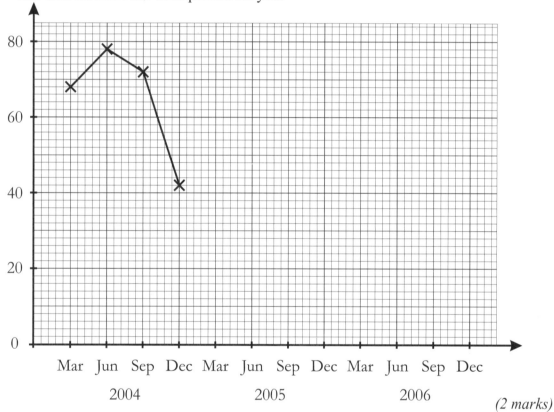

(2 marks)

(b) Calculate the four-point moving average and plot it on the same graph.

....
....
....
....
....*(3 marks)*

(c) Comment on your graph.

....
....*(2 marks)*

H12 This cumulative frequency curve shows the lengths of time that some people spent in a supermarket.

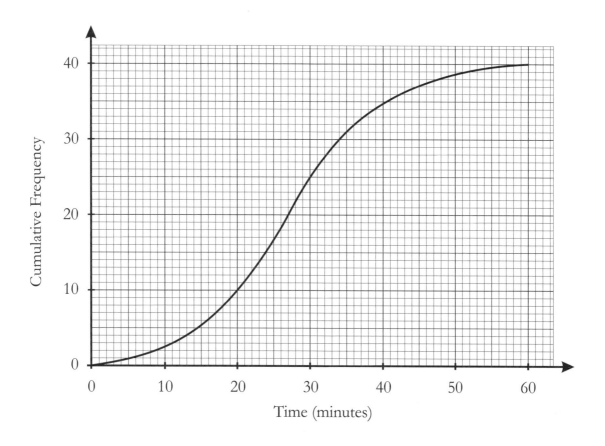

(a) How many people took part in the survey?

Answer..people *(1 mark)*

(b) Find the median time spent in the supermarket.

Answer... minutes *(2 marks)*

(c) How many people spent longer than 20 minutes in the supermarket?

....

Answer... people *(2 marks)*

(d) Find the interquartile range.

....

....

Answer... minutes *(3 marks)*

Handling Data

H13 The graph shows the amount of money spent on eating out, by a group of families each month.

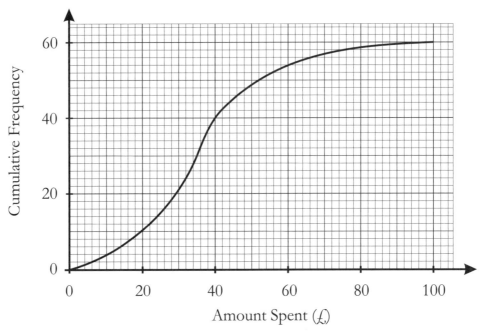

(a) Find the median amount spent.

Answer £...(2 marks)

(b) What percentage of families spent less than £40 per month on eating out?

....

....

Answer.. % (2 marks)

H14 The times taken by 160 people to complete an IQ test are shown, in minutes, in the table on the left below.

(a) Fill in the cumulative frequency table on the right. *(1 mark)*

Time (t minutes)	Frequency
$40 \leqslant t < 50$	8
$50 \leqslant t < 60$	28
$60 \leqslant t < 70$	64
$70 \leqslant t < 80$	40
$80 \leqslant t < 90$	15
$90 \leqslant t < 100$	5

Time (t minutes)	Cumulative Frequency
$t < 40$	0
$t < 50$	
$t < 60$	
$t < 70$	
$t < 80$	
$t < 90$	
$t < 100$	

(b) Draw a cumulative frequency curve for the data, using the graph paper provided.

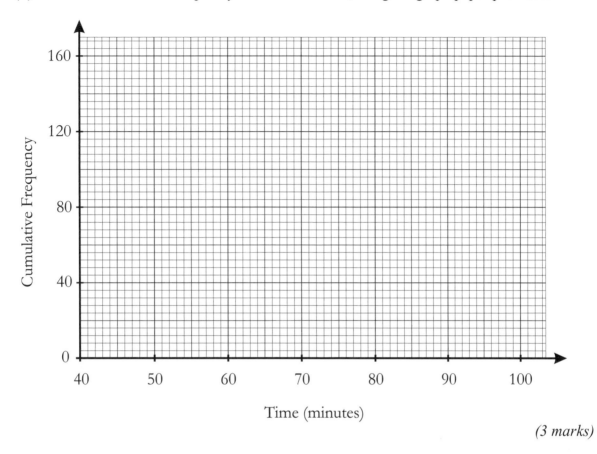

(3 marks)

(c) Estimate the median.

Answer...minutes *(2 marks)*

(d) Use your graph to estimate the number of people who took longer than 65 minutes.

....

Answer...people *(2 marks)*

(e) Find the interquartile range.

....

....

Answer...minutes *(3 marks)*

Handling Data

H15 Inder drew this box-and-whisker diagram to show the length of time that people spent waiting to connect to the internet.

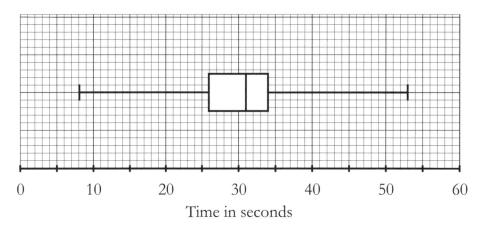

Time in seconds

Complete this table.

	Minimum	Maximum	Median	Lower quartile	Upper quartile
Time in seconds					

(3 marks)

H16 The speeds in miles per hour of 11 tennis serves were recorded.
The speeds were:

90, 68, 95, 121, 56, 78, 83, 109, 86, 76, 63

(a) Find the lower and upper quartiles for the data.

....

....

Lower quartile = ...

Upper quartile = ...*(2 marks)*

(b) Draw a box-and-whisker diagram to show the data.

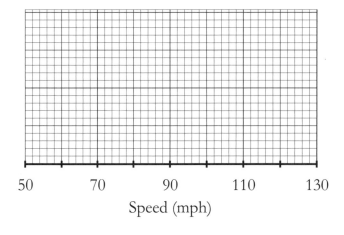

Speed (mph)

(3 marks)

H17 John carried out a survey of 60 pupils in his year at school.
He wanted to know how many books they had each bought in the last year.
The frequency table shows his data.

Number of books	Frequency	Angle of Sector
0 to 2	12	
3 to 5	32	
6 to 8	11	
9 or more	5	

(a) Construct a pie chart to show this information.

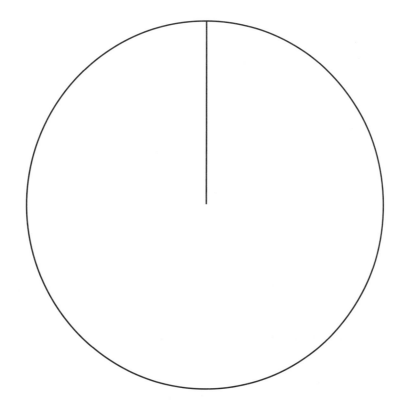

(5 marks)

(b) What fraction of the pupils bought 3, 4 or 5 books?
Write your fraction in its lowest terms.

....

....

Answer...*(2 marks)*

Handling Data

Scatter Graphs

H18 The table shows the prices of nine cars, together with their top speeds in mph.

Price (£1000s)	12	26	32	15	18	8	22	41	43
Top Speed (mph)	90	114	124	93	101	85	111	131	139

(a) On the grid below, draw a scatter graph to show this information.
The first five points have been plotted for you.

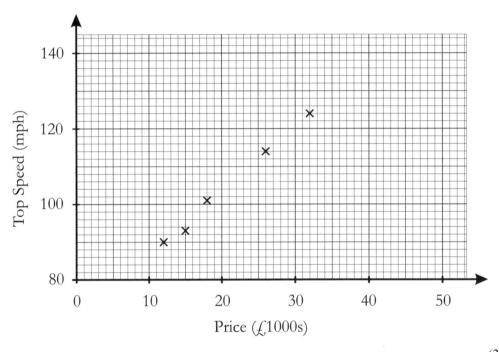

(2 marks)

(b) Describe the correlation between the prices of these cars and their top speeds.

.... *(1 mark)*

(c) Draw a line of best fit on your scatter graph. *(1 mark)*

(d) Use your line of best fit to estimate:

(i) the price of a car with a top speed of 120 mph,

Answer £... *(1 mark)*

(ii) the top speed of a car costing £25 000.

Answer .... mph *(1 mark)*

H19 The table shows the heights of some fully grown tomato plants and the amount of Thunder Growth Feed given to them each day.

Amount (ml)	23	8	10	22	14	15	21	12	19	16
Height (cm)	10	37	31	12	23	22	14	27	16	20

(a) On the grid below, draw a scatter graph to show this information.
The first four points have been plotted for you.

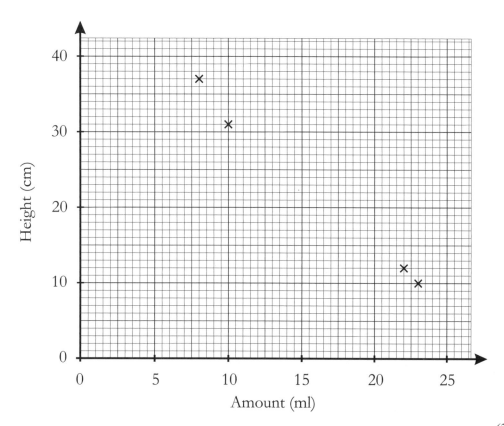

Amount (ml)

(3 marks)

(b) Draw a line of best fit on your scatter graph. *(1 mark)*

(c) Use your line to estimate the height of a fully grown tomato plant fed 20 ml of Thunder Growth Feed each day.

Answer.. cm *(1 mark)*

(d) Describe the correlation between the amount of Thunder Growth Feed given and the height.

.... *(1 mark)*

Handling Data

H20 The table and histogram show how long (in minutes) 100 people spent watching television one evening.

Time (t minutes)	Frequency
$0 \leqslant t < 15$	10
$15 \leqslant t < 30$	
$30 \leqslant t < 60$	40
$60 \leqslant t < 120$	
$120 \leqslant t < 180$	10
$t > 180$	0

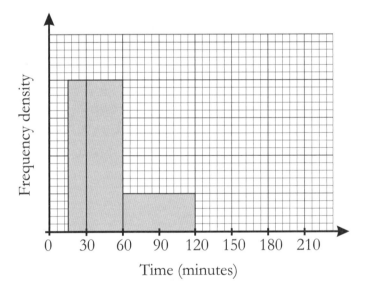

(a) Use the information in the histogram to complete the table. *(3 marks)*

(b) Use the information in the table to complete the histogram. *(2 marks)*

H21 The table shows the lengths of time that people waited to use a cash machine one morning.

Time (x seconds)	Frequency
$0 \leqslant x < 5$	10
$5 \leqslant x < 15$	16
$15 \leqslant x < 25$	18
$25 \leqslant x < 30$	20
$30 \leqslant x < 50$	36
$50 \leqslant x < 60$	12

On the grid, draw a histogram to represent this information.

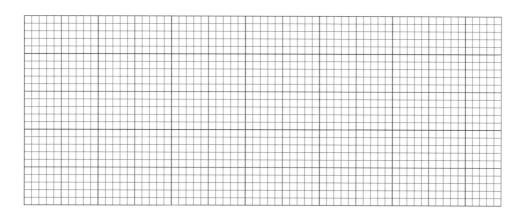

(5 marks)

H22 A bag contains red, green and black beads. If a bead is removed from the bag at random, the probability that it is red is 0.2 and the probability that it is green is 0.6.

(a) What is the probability of removing a black bead?

....

....

Answer ....*(2 marks)*

There are 120 beads altogether in the bag.

(b) How many of the beads are green?

....

....

Answer ....*(2 marks)*

Handling Data

H23 A biased dice, with faces numbered 1, 2, 3, 4, 5 and 6, is thrown 500 times.
The results are shown in the table below.

Number	1	2	3	4	5	6
Frequency	45	248	2	55	94	56

(a) Estimate the probability that the next time the dice is thrown it will show a 2.

....

Answer.. *(1 mark)*

Estimate the probability that the next time the dice is thrown it will show:

(b) an odd number,

....

....

Answer.. *(2 marks)*

(c) a number greater than 4.

....

....

Answer.. *(2 marks)*

H24 Steven always has one piece of fruit with his lunch. The table below shows the probability
that he has a particular fruit with his lunch.

Apple	Pear	Banana	Peach	Grapes
0.3	0.2	0.1	0.3	0.1

(a) Calculate the probability of Steven not having an apple with his lunch.

....

Answer.. *(1 mark)*

(b) Calculate the probability of Steven having an apple or a pear.

....

....

Answer..*(2 marks)*

H25 Sandra has estimated the probabilities of it raining on particular days of the year. Her estimates are shown in the table below.

St Valentine's Day	Easter Sunday	May Day	Christmas Day
0.5	0.3	0.2	0.7

(a) Use the table to calculate the probability of it not raining on May Day.

....

Answer... *(1 mark)*

(b) Calculate the probability of it raining on Easter Sunday and Christmas Day.

....

....

Answer...*(2 marks)*

(c) Calculate the probability of it not raining on St Valentine's Day and not raining on Christmas Day.

....

....

Answer...*(2 marks)*

H26 Bethany has a cold. The probability that her sister Megan will catch a cold is 0.42. The probability that her brother Jack will catch a cold is 0.16.

(a) What is the probability that both Megan and Jack will catch colds?

....

....

Answer...*(2 marks)*

(b) What is the probability that neither of them will catch colds?

....

....

....

Answer...*(3 marks)*

(c) What is the probability that at least one of them will catch a cold?

....

....

Answer...*(2 marks)*

Handling Data

H27 Roberta has two biased dice. The probability that dice *A* will land on a six is 0.25. The probability that dice *B* will land on a six is 0.12. Roberta throws both dice just once.

(a) What is the probability of Roberta throwing two sixes?

....

....

Answer..*(2 marks)*

(b) What is the probability that Roberta will throw no more than one six?

....

....

Answer..*(2 marks)*

H28 A bag contains 6 green balls, 4 red balls and 2 blue balls.

(a) If two balls are picked at random, what is the probability that they are both blue?

....

....

Answer..*(2 marks)*

(b) If three balls are picked at random, what is the probability that two of them are blue?

....

....

....

....

Answer..*(3 marks)*

H29 Six cards from an ordinary pack of playing cards have been placed face down on a table. Three of the cards are aces, two are red queens and one is the king of spades.

(a) If a card is picked out at random, what is the probability that it is the queen of hearts?

....

Answer.. *(1 mark)*

(b) If three cards are picked at random, what is the probability that two of them are red queens?

....

....

....

....

Answer..*(3 marks)*

Gareth randomly selects a card and removes it from the table.

(c) If Pam now selects three cards, what is the probability that they are all aces?

....

....

....

....

Answer...*(3 marks)*

H30 Charlotte and Brian usually go shopping together on Friday evenings.
The probability that Charlotte goes shopping on any particular Friday evening is 0.96.
If Charlotte goes shopping, the probability that Brian will go as well is 0.82.
If Charlotte doesn't go, the probability that Brian will still go is 0.68.

(a) Use the above information to complete the tree diagram.

Charlotte   **Brian**

(3 marks)

(b) What is the probability that Brian will go shopping alone?

....

....

Answer...*(2 marks)*

(c) What is the probability that at least one of them will go shopping?

....

....

....

Answer...*(3 marks)*

Handling Data

H31 Robina, Suzy, Roger and Harry are playing a board game. The probabilities of Robina, Suzy, Roger or Harry being first to complete a circuit of the board are as follows:

Robina	Suzy	Roger	Harry
0.25	0.32	0.17	0.26

After the first circuit, the player who completed the circuit first has a probability of 0.45 of winning.

(a) Use the information above to complete the tree diagram.

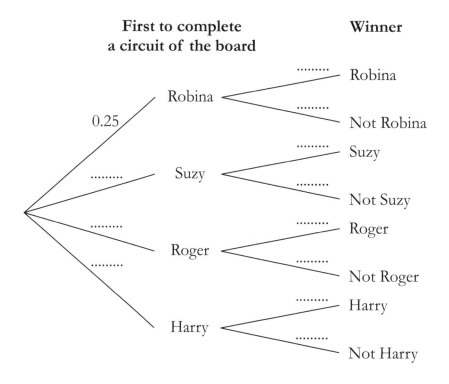

(3 marks)

(b) Calculate the probability that Suzy will be the first to complete a circuit, yet lose the game.

....

....

Answer ....*(2 marks)*

H32 Suna wants to find out how often people use public transport.
He has written three questions to use in a questionnaire.

> **1** What is your name? _____
>
> **2** Do you agree public transport is less convenient than using a car?
> ☐ yes   ☐ no   ☐ don't know
>
> **3** How many times a month do you use public transport?
> ☐ never   ☐ hardly ever   ☐ occasionally   ☐ often

(a) What is wrong with the first question on the questionnaire?

....

.... *(1 mark)*

(b) What is wrong with Suna's second question?

....

.... *(1 mark)*

(c) What is wrong with the choices offered for the third question?
Explain how the choices could be improved.

....

....

.... *(1 mark)*

H33 A health authority is conducting a survey to find
out how often people visit the dentist.
To do this they decide to take a sample of 1000 people.

(a) Describe how the health authority might select a random sample.

....

.... *(2 marks)*

(b) Suggest another sampling method which might more accurately reflect the population.

.... *(1 mark)*

(c) Explain how the health authority could use the sampling method you suggested in **(b)**.

....

....

.... *(2 marks)*

Answers

N1 (a) £301.32 (b) 27

N2 (a) £527.62 (b) 31

N3 $\frac{24}{360} = \frac{1}{15}$

N4 $\frac{5}{30} = \frac{1}{6}$

N5 (a) $\frac{1}{5}$ (b) $\frac{3}{10}$ (c) $\frac{3}{8}$

N6 (a) $\frac{4}{5}$ (b) $\frac{5}{8}$ (c) $\frac{2}{15}$

N7 $3\frac{19}{24}$

N8 (a) $\frac{15}{100} = \frac{3}{20}$ (b) 15

(c) 0.0015 (d) 32

N9 $\frac{31}{99}$

N10 $\frac{426}{999} = \frac{142}{333}$

N11 (a) −10 (b) −2

(c) −27 (d) −3

N12 (a) 2 (b) 2

(c) 36 (d) 4

N13 (a) 70% (b) 30%

N14 £2.28

N15 (a) £10 200 (b) £8670

N16 £449.44

N17 12.9%

N18 23.8%

N19 (a) £62 609 (b) £71 579

N20 £1091

N21 32.25%

N22 (a) £22 (b) 60%

N23 £10

N24 120 g

N25 480 g

N26 (a) 252 (b) $2 \times 3^2 \times 5$

N27 (a) 2, 4, 6, 10 (b) 2, 10

(c) $x = 10, y = 6$

N28 (a) 84 (b) 4

N29 28 m

N30 (a) (i) $2^2 \times 3 \times 5$ (ii) $2^2 \times 3 \times 7$

(b) 12 (c) 420

N31 (a) 64 (b) 4

(c) 81 (d) 16

N32 (a) 4.83 (b) 1.58 (c) 0.422

N33 (a) $\frac{1}{2}$ (b) 8 (c) 25

N34 $y = 0$

N35 $x = 2$

N36 (a) 27 (b) 9, 16

(c) 10 (d) $x = 9, y = 27$

N37 $x = 3, y = 13, z = 16$

N38 (a) $2\sqrt{5}$ (b) $7\sqrt{3}$

N39 (a) $2\pi, \sqrt{12}$ (b) e.g. $14.44 (= 3.8^2)$

(c) e.g. $\sqrt{3}$ and $\frac{1}{\sqrt{3}}$

N40 (a) $7\sqrt{5}$ (b) $9\sqrt{2} + 2$

N41 (a) $3\sqrt{2}$ (b) $5 + 2\sqrt{3}$

N42 (a) 1.222 (b) 1.22

N43 (a) $\frac{80 + 20}{30 - 10} = 5$

(b) Surface area $\approx 4 \times 3 \times 5^2 = 300$ m^2
There won't be enough paint.

N44 (a) $\frac{400 \times 0.5}{40} = 5$

(b) Surface area $\approx 6 \times 30^2 = 5400$ cm^2
There won't be enough paint.

N45 0.022 to 2 s.f.

N46 1.7 to 1 d.p.

N47 (a) 9.2×10^5 (b) 4 300 000

N48 (a) 4.42×10^5 (b) 6.37×10^6

N49 2×10^8

N50 6.6×10^3

N51 (a) 3.84×10^5 km

(b) $(3.84 \times 10^5) \div (3.5 \times 10^3) = 110$ Moon diameters

N52 (a) $(6.2 \times 10^2) \times (7.4 \times 10^{-3}) = 4.6$ cm (to 2 s.f.)

(b) $(4.2 \times 10^2) \div (6.2 \times 10^2)$
$= 0.68$ g or 6.8×10^{-1} g (to 2 s.f.)

N53 (a) 13 (b) 3.3

A1 $50x + 75y$

A2 (a) a^6 (b) $10x^4y^8$ (c) $27x^{12}y^3$

A3 (a) $x = 1\frac{1}{5}$ (b) $x = 4$ (c) $x = 1$

A4 (a) $x = 2$ (b) $x = 15$ (c) $x = 15$

A5 (a) $y = 3$ (b) $y = 2$ (c) $y = 12$

A6 (a) $4x + 8 = 32$ (b) £6

A7 (a) $4y + 12 = 852$ (b) 210 g

A8 (a) 15 (b) 32

A9 (a) $\frac{2}{9}$ (b) 11

A10 (a) $P = 6H + 2S$ (b) £412

A11 $a = \sqrt{b - 2}$

A12 $x = \frac{y^{1/3} - 4}{3}$

A13 (a) $a = \frac{v^2 - u^2}{2s}$ (b) $u = \sqrt{v^2 - 2as}$

A14 (a) $3x^4$ (b) $\frac{x^2 + 2x}{6}$

A15 (a) $2x^2$ (b) $\frac{x^2}{2}$ (c) $x = 6$

A16 $x = 1$

A17 (a) $a = \frac{c}{bc - 1}$ (b) $\frac{13x + 6}{(x + 2)(x - 3)}$

A18 (a) $x = \frac{1 + y}{yz}$ (b) $\frac{16x + 6}{(x + 1)(2x + 1)}$

A19 **(a)** (0, 2.5) **(b)** −0.5

(c)

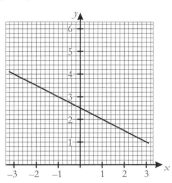

A20 **(a)**

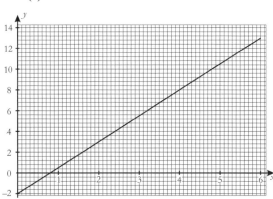

(b) $y = 5$ **(c)** $x = 5.2$

A21

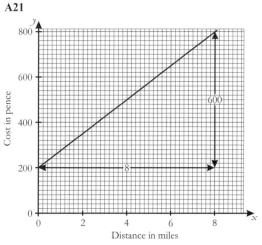

(a) Gradient $= \dfrac{600}{8} = 75$,
  y-intercept $= 200$,
  so $y = 75x + 200$.

(b) $75 \times 10 + 200 = 950\text{p} = £9.50$

A22 **(a)** $6y = 3x + 8$ **(b)** $2y + 4x = 3$

A23 $y = 3x - 3$

A24 $y = 17 - 4x$

A25 **(a)** $x = 2$, $y = 1$

(b) **(i)**

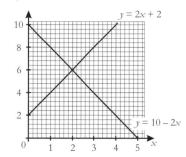

(ii) The graphs meet where $x = 2$.

A26 **(a)** $x = 3$, $y = 1$

(b) **(i) (ii)**

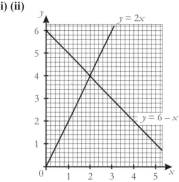

(iii) The graphs meet where $y = 4$.

A27 $x = -4.5$, $y = 4$

A28 $x = -2$, $y = 3$

A29 **(a)** $x^2 + y^2 = 16$ **(b)** $(0, 4), (4, 0)$

A30 $(0, 5), (3, 4)$

A31 $x = 2, y = -5$ or $x = 3, y = -3$

A32 $-5, -4, -3, -2, -1, 0, 1, 2, 3$

A33 $-1, 0, 1, 2, 3, 4, 5, 6$

A34 **(a)**

(b)

A35 **(a)** $x < \dfrac{1}{2}$

(b)

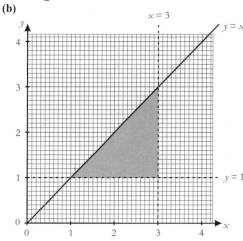

Answers

A36 (a) $x < 3\frac{1}{13}$

(b) (i) (ii)

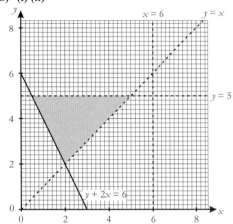

(iii) (1, 4), (2, 3), (2, 4), (3, 4)

A37 $x = 7.9$ to 1 d.p.

A38 $x = 3.2$ to 1 d.p.

A39 (a) $6m + 11n$ (b) $3(3b - 2)$ (c) $5x(x - 2)$

A40 (a) $2x^2 - 5x - 63$ (b) $(x + 2)(x + 4)$

A41 (a) $15x^2 + 2x - 8$ (b) $(2x - 1)(x + 3)$

A42 $(x + 5y)(x - 5y)$

A43 $(3x + 4y)(3x - 4y)$

A44 $(x + 3)^2 + 3$

A45 $x^2 - 14x + 10 = (x - 7)^2 - 39$, so $a = 7$, $b = 39$

A46 $x + 3y$

A47 $\dfrac{x}{x - 1}$

A48 (a) $x(x + 3)$ (b) $x = 0$ or -3

A49 (a) $x(x - 4)$ (b) $x = 0$ or 4

A50 (a) $(x - 4)(x + 3)$ (b) $x = 4$ or -3

A51 (a) $(x - 5)(x + 2)$ (b) $x = 5$ or -2

A52 (a) area $MNOP$ = area $ABCD$
$x \times (x + 2) = 1 \times (x + 6)$
$x^2 + 2x = x + 6$
$x^2 + x - 6 = 0$

(b) $MP = 2$ cm (-3 cm is a nonsensical solution)

A53 (a) $(16 - x)$ cm

(b) length × width = area
$x(16 - x) = 48$
$16x - x^2 = 48$
$x^2 - 16x + 48 = 0$

(c) Possible lengths are 4 cm and 12 cm.

A54 (a) $(x - 2)^2 + (x - 1)^2 = x^2$
giving $x^2 - 6x + 5 = 0$

(b) 5 cm ($x = 1$ gives a nonsensical solution)

A55 $x = 1.43$ or 0.23

A56 $x = -2.45$ or 0.204

A57 (a)

x	-2	-1	0	1	2	3
y	21	5	-3	-3	5	21

(b)

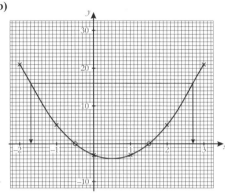

(c) (i) $x = -0.5$ or 1.5 (read off at $y = 0$)

(ii) $x = -1.7$ or 2.7 (read off at $y = 16$)

(d) $y = -4$

A58 (a)

x	-3	-2	-1	0	1	2	3
y	14	7	2	-1	-2	-1	2

(b)

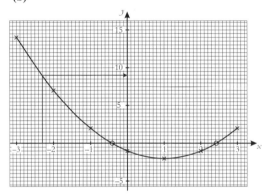

(c) $y = 9$

(d) $x = -0.4$ or 2.4

A59 (a)

x	-3	-2	-1	0	1	2	3
y	-26	-7	0	1	2	9	28

(b)

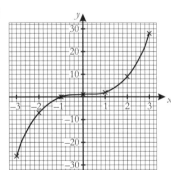

(c) (i) $x = -2.2$

(ii) If $x^3 = 19$
then $x^3 + 1 = 20$
so $x = 2.7$ (reading off at $y = 20$)

A60 (a)

x	–3	–2	–1	0	1	2	3
y	29	10	3	2	1	–6	–25

(b)

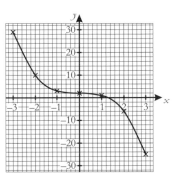

(c) (i) $x = -2.6$ (ii) $x = 1.3$

A61 (a) 11:20 (b) 10 minutes (c) 2.5 km

(d)

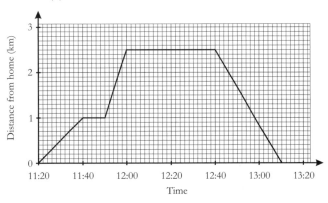

(e) 5 km/h

A62 (a) Pippa

(b) 20 m (after 2 seconds)

(c) She stopped, perhaps after falling over.

(d) Pippa, she overtook Sarah.

A63 (a) 16.5 m/s

(b) 3 m/s ÷ 75 s = 0.04 m/s^2

A64 Graph B cannot be $y = x^2 + 2$ because it cuts the y-axis at the origin, not at $y = 2$.

A65

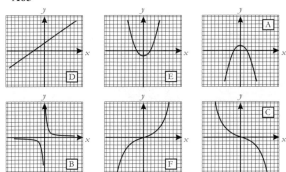

A66 Vase A matches graph 4
Vase B matches graph 3
Vase C matches graph 2
Vase D matches graph 1

A67 (a) Graph 1 (b) Graph 4
(c) Graph 2 (d) Graph 3

A68 (a)

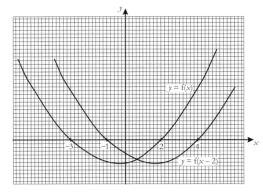

(b) $(0, -18)$

A69 (a)

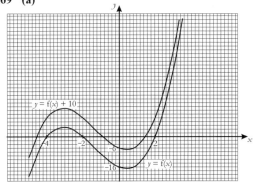

(b) $y = -x^3 + 4x^2 + 4x - 16$

A70 (a) $5n - 3$ (b) $10 - 2n$

A71 (a) $4n - 1$ (b) $13 - 3n$

A72 (a) $5 + (6 \times 7)$

(b) $n + (n + 1)(n + 2) = n^2 + 4n + 2$

A73 (a) $(7 \times 8)^2$

(b) $n^2(n + 1)^2 = n^4 + 2n^3 + n^2$

A74 (a) (i) $a = \frac{8}{6}b = 13\frac{1}{3}$ (ii) $b = \frac{6}{8}a = 49\frac{1}{2}$

(b)

x	2	5	20	10
y	50	8	$\frac{1}{2}$	2

A75 (a)

p	2	3	5	10
q	80	180	500	2000

(b) (i) 40 minutes
(ii) 2 painters

Answers

SHAPE, SPACE & MEASURES

S1 56 cm

S2 32 cm²

S3 18.9 m²

S4 15.4 cm

S5 (400 − 100π) cm²

S6 (a) 15 cm²   (b) 300 cm³

S7 (a) 84 000 cm² (b) 417 000 mm³

S8 148π cm²

S9 314.2 − 110 = 204.2 cm³

S10 26.9 cm

S11 6.0 cm

S12 2145 cm³

S13 15.5 cm

S14 A surface area is always length × length, whereas this formula is length × length × length, which is typical of a volume formula.

S15 Formula D because it is the only formula where all the terms are length × length × length.

S16

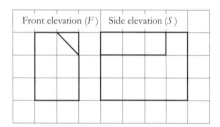

S17 (a) x and 60° are corresponding angles and so are equal.

  (b) 60°

S18 (a) a and 50° are alternate angles and so are equal.

  (b) 130°

S19 (a) x and 120° are supplementary angles and so add up to 180°.

  (b) 120°

S20 (a) Angles at a point add up to 360°, so a + 40° = 360°.

  (b) 140°

S21 (a) (number of sides − 2) × 180° = 720°

  (b) 120°

S22 x = 110°

S23 (a)

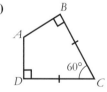

  (b) 120°

S24 (a) 31.4 cm   (b) 2.6 cm   (c) 6.5 cm²

S25 16.6 cm

S26 (a) 9.5 cm   (b) 60°   (c) 168 cm²

S27 (a) 38°   (b) 142°

S28 (a) 72°   (b) 18°

S29 (a) 52°

  (b) 52°
      Angles subtended at the circumference by the same arc are equal.

S30 (a) 32°   (b) 58°

S31 5.5 cm

S32 6.3 cm

S33 1204 m

S34 (a) (3.5, 1)   (b) 5 units

S35 26.4° (using sin)

S36 64.6° (using cos)

S37 (a) 3.2 m   (b) 43°

S38 (a) 2.9 m   (b) 7.8 m

S39 (a)

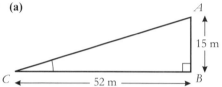

  (b) 16.1°

S40 (a) 658 cm²   (b) 42.8 cm

S41 (a) 70°   (b) 358 m²

S42 (a) 14.1 cm   (b) 69.3°   (c) 37.4 cm

S43 (a) 70°   (b) 5.5 cm   (c) 11.6 cm

S44 (a)

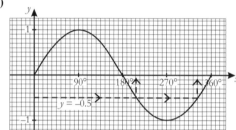

  (b) 210° and 330°

S45 78.46° and 281.54°

S46 (a)

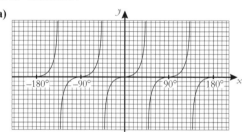

  (b) −180°, −90°, 0°, 90°, 180°

S47 4.8 cm

S48 (a) 4.3 m   (b) 150°

S49 (a) $\begin{pmatrix} 6 \\ 2 \end{pmatrix}$ (b) $\begin{pmatrix} 6 \\ 7 \end{pmatrix}$

S50 (a) $\begin{pmatrix} -5 \\ 3 \end{pmatrix}$ (b) $\begin{pmatrix} 12 \\ -5 \end{pmatrix}$

S51 (a) (i) a + c   (ii) a − b

  (b) a = $\frac{1}{3}$ (b − c)

S52 (a) (i) a + b   (ii) c − a − b

  (b) 2a − c + b

S53 (a) Reflection in the x-axis

  (b) Translation $\begin{pmatrix} -5 \\ 0 \end{pmatrix}$

S54 **(a)** 180° rotation about (4, 0)

(b)

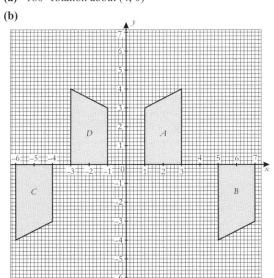

(c) For example, 180° rotation about (–2, 0) followed by a reflection in the line $x = -3.5$. Many other combinations are possible.

S55 **(a) & (b)**

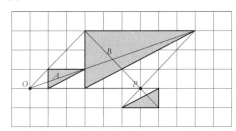

S56 **(a)** $\frac{1}{2}$

(b)

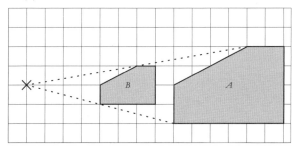

S57 25 000 m

S58 110 pounds

S59 400 m ÷ 48.6 s = 8.2 m/s

S60 182 miles ÷ 3.5 h = 52 mph

S61 3.2 m/s × 480 s = 1536 m = 1.536 km

S62 5000 kg ÷ 1.2 m³ = 4167 kg/m³

S63 25 000 kg ÷ 200 kg/m³ = 125 m³

S64 **(a)** 32.495 kg   **(b)** 32.485 kg

S65 **(a)** 52.45 m   **(b)** 52.35 m

S66 Upper bound = 7.25 × 4.55 = 32.9875 cm²
Lower bound = 7.15 × 4.45 = 31.8175 cm²

S67 **(a)** $\frac{4.655}{2.45\pi} = 0.6048$ cm

(b) $\frac{1}{3}\pi \times 9.575^2 \times 2.425 = 232.8$ cm³

S68 **(a)** 2000 m

(b)

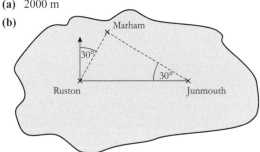

S69 **(a)** 600 m

(b)

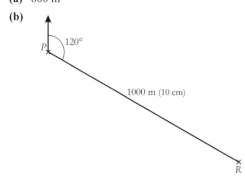

S70 **(a)** 100°

(b)

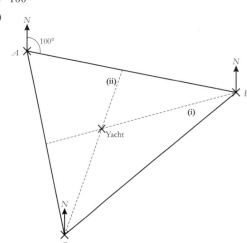

S71 **(a)** 249°   **(b)** 13 km

(c)

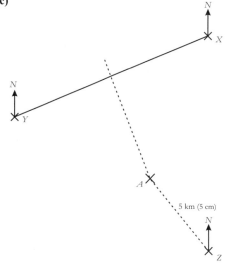

Answers

S72

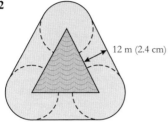

12 m (2.4 cm)

S73

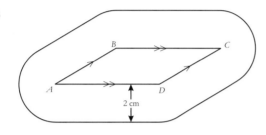

2 cm

HANDLING DATA

H1 (a) (i) 14 mm   (ii) 87 mm

(b) The beef tomatoes are generally larger in diameter than the plum tomatoes, and are a more consistent size.

H2 (a) 78 kg   (b) 74 kg

(c) The mode, it's the lowest weight.

H3 (a) £546.63   (b) £56

(c) The mean does not give a good indication, it is distorted by an extreme value (£4002).

H4 (a) Mean = 54 ÷ 40 = 1.35 goals

(b) Mode = 1 goal

H5 (a) 1.72 eggs   (b) 1 egg   (c) 1.5 eggs

H6 (a) Class $40 < t \leqslant 60$ because the median is the 25th value, which is in this class.

(b) $20 < t \leqslant 40$

(c) 46 seconds

H7 (a)

Height (h cm)	Tally	Frequency
$40 \leqslant h < 44$	||	2
$44 \leqslant h < 48$	⣿	5
$48 \leqslant h < 52$	⣿ ||	7
$52 \leqslant h < 56$	⣿ ||	7
$56 \leqslant h < 60$	|||	3

(b)

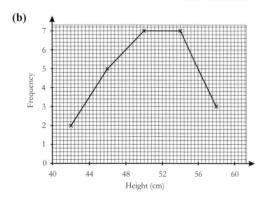

H8 (a)

Time (T mins)	Tally	Frequency
$30 \leqslant T < 36$	|||	3
$36 \leqslant T < 42$	⣿	5
$42 \leqslant T < 48$	⣿ ⣿ |	11
$48 \leqslant T < 54$	⣿ |||	8
$54 \leqslant T < 60$	|||	3

(b)

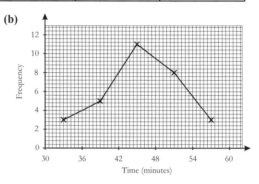

H9 (a)

1	3	4				
2	0	3	4	6	6	9
3	0	1	3	4	6	8
4	2	2	2	6	8	9

(b) 42   (c) 32

H10 (a)

6	4	4	5	7	8	8	9		
7	0	0	1	1	2	2	2	2	3
8	1	3	7	7	9				
9	0	1	5						

(b) 72

H11 (a)

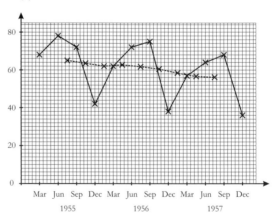

(b) The four-point moving averages are: 65, 63.5, 62, 62.75, 61.75, 60.5, 58.5, 56.75, 56.25

(c) The trend is slightly downwards. This could be due to falling sales or perhaps an increase in automation.

H12 **(a)** 40 people **(b)** 27 minutes

(c) 30 people **(d)** 14 minutes

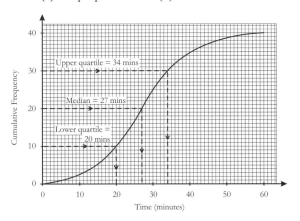

H13 **(a)** £35 **(b)** 66.7%

H14 **(a)**

Time (t minutes)	Cumulative Frequency
$t < 40$	0
$t < 50$	8
$t < 60$	36
$t < 70$	100
$t < 80$	140
$t < 90$	155
$t < 100$	160

(b)

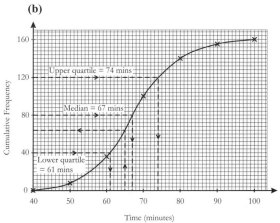

(c) 67 minutes

(d) 96 people

(e) 13 minutes

H15

	Minimum	Maximum	Median	Lower quartile	Upper quartile
Time in seconds	8	53	31	26	34

H16 **(a)** Lower quartile = 68, Upper quartile = 95

(b)

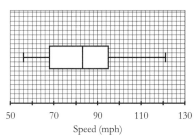

H17 **(a)**

Number of books	Angle of Sector
0 to 2	72°
3 to 5	192°
6 to 8	66°
9 or more	30°
	360°

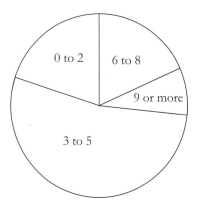

(b) $\frac{8}{15}$

H18 **(a) & (c)**

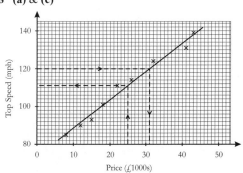

(b) Strong positive correlation

(d) **(i)** £31 000

(ii) 111 mph

Answers

HANDLING DATA

H19 (a) & (b)

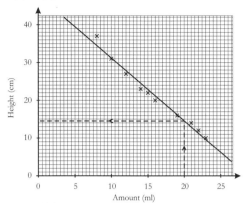

(c) 14.5 cm

(d) Strong negative correlation

H20 (a)

Time (*t* minutes)	Frequency
$0 \leqslant t < 15$	10
$15 \leqslant t < 30$	20
$30 \leqslant t < 60$	40
$60 \leqslant t < 120$	20
$120 \leqslant t < 180$	10
$t > 180$	0

(b)

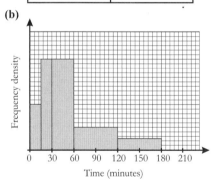

H21

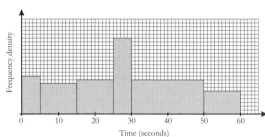

H22 (a) 0.2   (b) 72

H23 (a) $\frac{62}{125}$ or 0.496   (b) $\frac{141}{500}$ or 0.282

     (c) $\frac{3}{10}$ or 0.3

H24 (a) 0.7   (b) 0.5

H25 (a) 0.8   (b) 0.21   (c) 0.15

H26 (a) 0.0672   (b) 0.4872   (c) 0.5128

H27 (a) 0.03   (b) 0.97

H28 (a) $\frac{1}{66}$ (b) $\frac{1}{22}$

H29 (a) $\frac{1}{6}$ (b) $\frac{1}{5}$ (c) $\frac{1}{20}$

H30 (a)

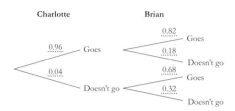

(b) 0.0272   (c) 0.9872

H31 (a)

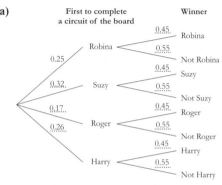

(b) $0.32 \times 0.55 = 0.176$

H32 (a) People may prefer to remain anonymous.

(b) The question is leading, as it encourages you to say 'yes'. Questions should never start 'Do you agree...'.

(c) The choices should be numbers. 'Occasionally', for example, may mean once a month to one person and once a week to another.

H33 (a) Any method where each member of the population is equally likely to be selected.

(b) Stratified sampling is most suitable.

(c) Divide the population into, for example, different age groups. Randomly select people from each age group (strata).